W9-CJT-055

BUILDING SOLUTIONS

A PROBLEM SOLVING GUIDE FOR BUILDERS AND RENOVATORS

CMHC offers a wide range of housing-related information. For details, call 1 800 668-2642 or visit our home page at www.cmhc.ca

Cette publication est aussi disponible en français sous le titre: Solutions de construction 61137

690.8 Bui

Building solutions.

PRICE: $34.95 (3559/ex)

Any reliance or action taken on the information, materials and techniques described in this book is the responsibility of the user. Readers are advised to evaluate the information, materials and techniques cautiously for themselves and to consult appropriate professional resources to determine whether information, materials and techniques are suitable in their case. CMHC assumes no responsibility for any consequences arising from the reader's use of the information, materials and techniques described.

Canadian Cataloguing in Publication Data

Main entry under title:

Building solutions: a problem solving guide for builders and renovators

Issued also in French under title: Solutions de construction.
Includes bibliographical references.
ISBN 0-660-17440-5
Cat. No. NH15-195/1998E

1.   House construction — Quality control.
2.   Dwellings — Remodelling — Quality control.
1.   Canada Mortgage and Housing Corporation.

TH4811.B84 1998   690'.   C98-980278-7

© 1998 Canada Mortgage and Housing Corporation
All rights reserved. No portion of this book may be reproduced, stored in a retrieval system or transmitted in any form or by any means, mechanical, electronic, photocopying, recording or otherwise without the prior written permission of Canada Mortgage and Housing Corporation. Without limiting the generality of the foregoing, no portion of this book may be translated from English into any other language without the prior written permission of Canada Mortgage and Housing Corporation.

Revised 2001, 2002, 2003
Printed in Canada
Produced by CMHC

CONTENTS

MAY 0 4 2004

Chapter 3 Wall Systems

Chapter 4 Roof and Ceiling Systems

Chapter 5 Indoor Air Quality and Ventilation

CHAPTER 6 NOISE CONTROL

PREFACE

This publication is designed to help builders reduce the expense and aggravation of construction defects and callbacks. By identifying the sources of the most common problems and by reviewing the problems themselves, you can focus on preventing deficiencies by improving procedures.

Building better is almost always less expensive in the long run—in financial terms and in terms of maintaining good client relations.

This publication can serve as a refresher for experienced builders. It can also warn you of the types of problems that might result from cutting corners, or from applying inadequate quality control procedures.

This is not a "how-to" manual. It assumes that you are familiar with the requirements of the National Building Code of Canada and with regional construction practices. In some cases, the solutions offered to common problems represent practices that exceed building code minimum requirements. In these instances, construction costs may be higher, but you may expect that the savings gained through fewer callbacks and repairs will justify the upgrades.

CHAPTER 1
Introduction

FOUNDATIONS

Basement cracks and leaks are among the most common sources of callbacks and warranty claims in new housing. Problems apply equally to poured concrete foundations and slabs, concrete block walls, and Preserved Wood Foundations (PWFs), and they usually reflect inadequate design and construction practices.

The cost of repairs to foundations almost always exceeds the cost of better construction practice.

This chapter identifies and provides solutions to many of the problems typically seen in the foundations of newly constructed houses. The solutions provided represent the better design and building practices being applied by leading builders and the best practical advice being offered by building researchers, professional associations, and the home building industry. In many cases, they reflect National Building Code of Canada (NBC) requirements; references are made to the 1995 NBC. In other instances, the solutions offered represent practices that go beyond the minimum requirements of the NBC, providing additional insurance against potential defects and callback costs.

Section 1.1 Concrete Foundation Walls
INTRODUCTION

Concrete foundations are the predominant foundation type in Canada. They encompass poured concrete walls and concrete block walls (slabs-on-ground are treated in section 1.3). When proper construction techniques are used, these two types of foundation can be durable and defect-free. However, when poor construction techniques are applied, costly construction defects are likely to result.

The major problems can be divided into two categories: those which result in structural deterioration and damage; and those which result in water leakage and moisture damage. The causes of their difficulties are often similar.

To reduce the likelihood of problems, builders must specify correct materials, use proper placement and curing procedures, and employ good drainage and moisture-control practices.

1.1.1 STRUCTURAL DETERIORATION AND DAMAGE

PROBLEM

CRACKS AND SPALLING FROM UNDERSTRENGTH CONCRETE

CAUSE

Insufficient design strength

While minimum standards for concrete strength are mandated in the NBC, construction practices and site conditions commonly result in reduced strength—either because water is added to the concrete on site or because weather conditions affect the concrete.

SOLUTIONS

Specify concrete with minimum compressive strength in excess of minimum NBC requirements, as illustrated below.

◆ To provide increased strength and improved watertightness, use 20-MPa (2 900-psi) concrete for foundation walls and basement slabs.

◆ Many builders recommend using concrete with a minimum strength of 30 MPa (4 350 psi) for garage slabs and other concrete exposed to freeze-thaw cycles.

◆ Air entrainment improves concrete durability and resistance to freeze-thaw cycles. The NBC requires 5 to 8 percent air entrainment for garage and carport floors and exterior steps.

◆ The NBC requires that concrete mixes not exceed a slump of 100 mm (4 in.) for slabs and 150 mm (6 in.) for walls.

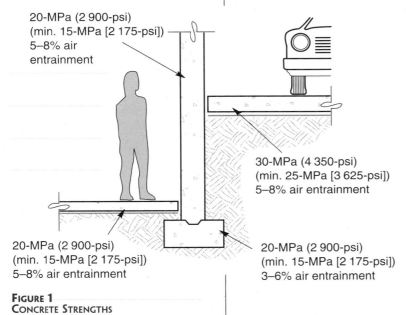

20-MPa (2 900-psi)
(min. 15-MPa [2 175-psi])
5–8% air
entrainment

20-MPa (2 900-psi)
(min. 15-MPa [2 175-psi])
5–8% air entrainment

30-MPa (4 350-psi)
(min. 25-MPa [3 625-psi])
5–8% air entrainment

20-MPa (2 900-psi)
(min. 15-MPa [2 175-psi])
3–6% air entrainment

FIGURE 1
CONCRETE STRENGTHS

PROBLEM
CRACKS AND SPALLING FROM UNDERDESIGNED CONCRETE

CAUSE

Inadequate dimensions

In some instances, builders will reduce the required size of footings and walls in an attempt to save on concrete costs. In other instances, slab thickness is inadvertently reduced below required minimums. Finally, reinforcing is often not installed in poor soil areas to enhance strength.

SOLUTIONS

Wall and footing thicknesses must meet NBC minimums, as illustrated below.

◆ In problem soils, or where a high water table exists, wall and footing thicknesses should be increased.

◆ A minimum slab thickness of 75 mm (3 in.) must be maintained, even where the slab slopes to a floor drain.

While not required by the NBC, wall and footing reinforcements in problem soils can minimize the potential for problems.

◆ Typical reinforcement may include two #10-m bars near the top of the foundation below window openings, or one bar located 300 mm (12 in.) from the top and one bar at grade.

◆ Footing reinforcement helps counteract uneven bearing conditions.

◆ Mesh reinforcement for slabs must be placed at, or slightly above, the mid-depth of the slab to be effective. Use flat sheets of mesh and maintain height with chairs or spacers.

◆ Fibreglass or polypropylene fibre mesh can reduce crack widths and surface spalling. Fibres are usually added to the mix at a rate of 1 kg/m^3 of concrete. The mesh must disperse well in the mix and must have good binding properties.

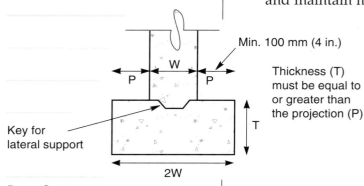

Min. 100 mm (4 in.)

Thickness (T) must be equal to or greater than the projection (P)

Key for lateral support

2W

FIGURE 2
FOOTING DIMENSION RELATIONSHIPS

PROBLEM
CRACKS IN FOUNDATIONS AND SLABS RESULTING FROM SETTLEMENT AND MOVEMENT

CAUSE

Inadequate bearing

Settlement and cracking are often caused by movement in the structure. When soil bearing is not adequate, problems are likely to occur.

SOLUTIONS

Ensure proper grade preparation.

◆ Where the sub-grade is disturbed, provide granular fill, ensuring acceptable consolidation and compaction.

◆ Never pour over frozen soils. In cold weather, pour as soon as possible after excavating, or provide frost protection. Keep concrete wet and warm for three days.

◆ Ensure proper compaction of granular fill over sewer lines running under footings. Ensure that service trenches are not located under foundation corners.

◆ The NBC requires that the vertical rise between stepped footings must not exceed 600 mm (24 in.) and the horizontal distance between risers shall be not less than 600 mm (24 in.). Provide generous filler to prevent shear failures at weak points in the footings.

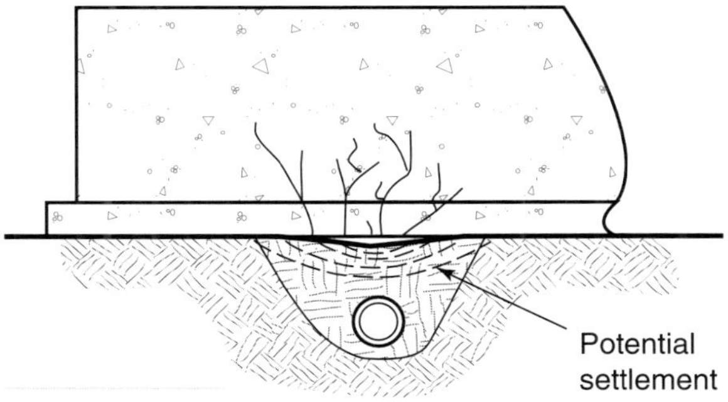

FIGURE 3
SETTLEMENT OVER UNDERGROUND SERVICES

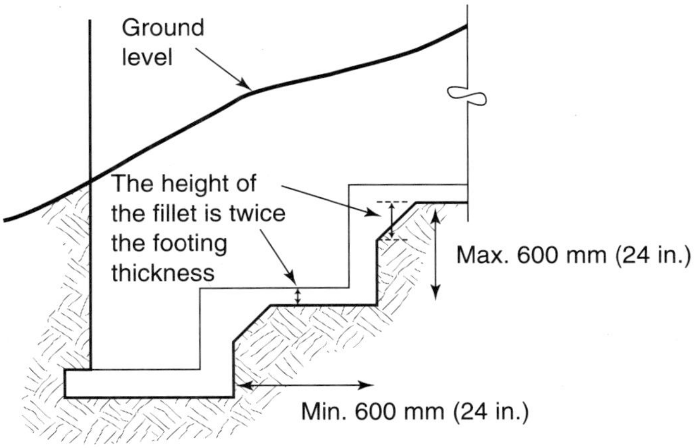

Potential settlement

Ground level

The height of the fillet is twice the footing thickness

Max. 600 mm (24 in.)

Min. 600 mm (24 in.)

FIGURE 4
STEPPED FOOTINGS

PROBLEM
CRACKS AND SPALLING FROM POOR CONSTRUCTION PRACTICES

CAUSE

Poor placement and finishing techniques

Improper placement and finishing techniques can result in a segregation of the fines and aggregates in the concrete mix.

SOLUTIONS

Proper preparation and placement

◆ Dampen the earth, and moisten or lubricate the forms to prevent the drawing of water from the concrete. Lubricate the forms before you erect them to prevent the lubricant from puddling on top of the footing.

◆ Place concrete within two hours of batching in cool weather and within one hour in hot weather.

◆ Use a puddling stick or vibrator to consolidate each lift, especially around openings, corners, and form ties.

◆ To prevent horizontal cold joints in walls, roughen the top of the previous pour, and puddle or vibrate the next pour (see Figure 5).

◆ To prevent cold joints in floor slabs, blend new concrete with previously placed concrete on the interface.

◆ Minimize concrete drops to prevent the segregation of aggregate. Excessive segregation will result in a loss of strength and the increased potential for water leakage. A maximum drop of 1.5 m (5 ft.) is recommended where reinforcing is used.

◆ Use chutes or buckets or pumped concrete to get concrete as close as possible to its final destination. Do not move concrete with a rake or vibrator, as segregation will result.

◆ Do not finish concrete when bleed water is present. Soak up the excess water with burlap or remove with a squeegee. Overtrowelling of the finished surface will result in the removal of air entrainment and further segregation of the fines, reducing the concrete's durability.

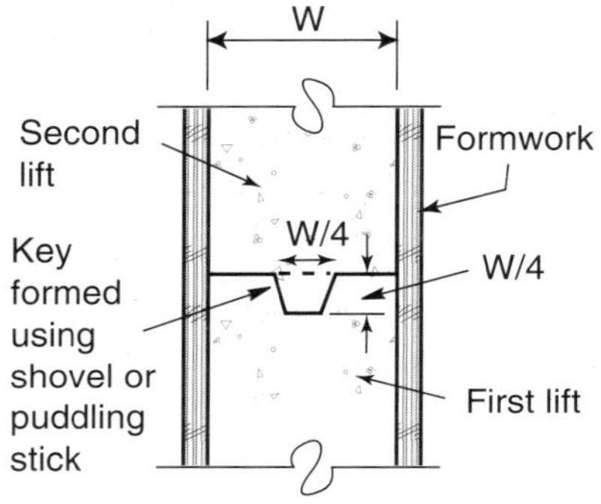

Second lift

Formwork

Key formed using shovel or puddling stick

First lift

FIGURE 5
HORIZONTAL CONSTRUCTION JOINT

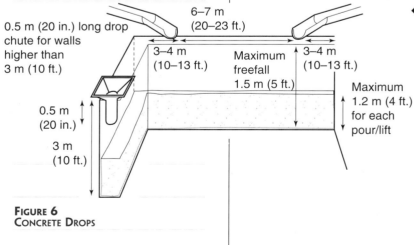

0.5 m (20 in.) long drop chute for walls higher than 3 m (10 ft.)

6–7 m (20–23 ft.)

3–4 m (10–13 ft.)

Maximum freefall 1.5 m (5 ft.)

3–4 m (10–13 ft.)

0.5 m (20 in.)

Maximum 1.2 m (4 ft.) for each pour/lift

3 m (10 ft.)

FIGURE 6
CONCRETE DROPS

PROBLEM
CRACKS AND SPALLING FROM POOR CONSTRUCTION PRACTICES

CAUSE

Overwatering

The addition of 4 L (1 gal.) of water to 1 m^3 (1.3 cubic yards) of concrete will decrease its strength by more than 1 MPa (145 psi) and increase slump by 25 mm (1 in.) (see Figure 7).

SOLUTIONS

Never add water on the construction site.

◆ Adding water alters the water–cement ratio of the mix, resulting in a loss of strength and the potential for increased shrinkage and reduced durability and watertightness.

◆ Where workability and movement of concrete around the site is expected to be a problem, use pumped concrete, or have the supplier increase the slump of the concrete by changing the proportions of the aggregate, by adding a super-plasticizer, or by increasing the percentage of air entrainment.

◆ Pour basements from a number of entry points to minimize the need to "flow" the concrete around the forms.

◆ Shovel or pump out wet sites to prevent standing water and mud from mixing with the poured concrete. Concrete should be placed on undisturbed soil or well-compacted fill.

CAUSE

Improper curing of concrete

Concrete will only reach its full design strength if it is allowed to cure properly in conditions that minimize the loss of the original water from the mixture. Where forms are stripped early, backfilling of the wall could prove disastrous if the concrete has not become strong enough.

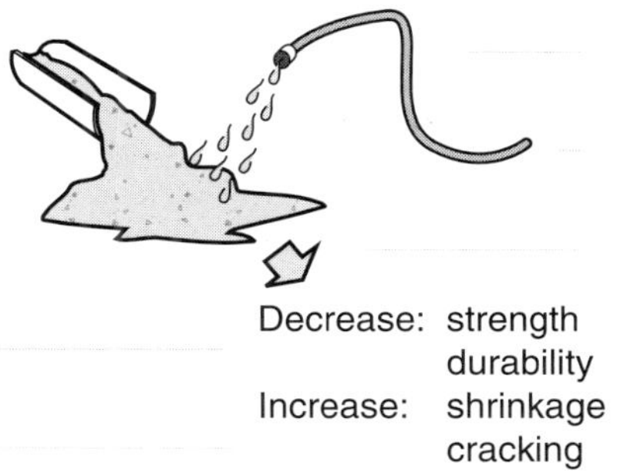

Decrease: strength
durability
Increase: shrinkage
cracking

FIGURE 7
EFFECTS OF OVERWATERING

Solutions

Moist-cure concrete for as long as possible.

◆ Keep concrete continuously moist unless formwork is left in place for a minimum of 24 hours. Improved performance will result from leaving formwork on for a minimum of two days, and it is recommended that slabs be moist-cured for a minimum of three days.

◆ Curing of foundation walls can be improved by
  – fogging or sprinkling them;
  – covering them with wet burlap or waterproof paper or material;
  – covering the exterior surfaces with curing compounds (following the manufacturers' recommendations); and
  – covering both the exterior and interior sides of the walls as soon as you remove the forms.

The combined effects of overwatering and improper curing can result in very weak concrete. For example, if you start with a design mix of 15 MPa (2 175 psi), add 18 L (4 gals.) of water per cubic metre on site, and strip forms within 18 hours, the resulting concrete will have a 28-day design strength of as low as 5 MPa (725 psi). Where proper curing practices are not followed, 30-MPa (4 350-psi) concrete should be used.

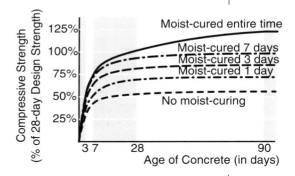

FIGURE 8
EFFECT OF CURING ON CONCRETE STRENGTH

PROBLEM
CRACKS AND SPALLING FROM POOR CONSTRUCTION PRACTICES

CAUSE

Inadequate cold weather protection—below 5°C (41°F)

Where concrete freezes before it is cured, it will suffer permanent loss of strength and watertightness.

SOLUTIONS

Provide cold weather protection strategies.

◆ Ensure qualified site supervision.

◆ Keep the temperature of the concrete above 10°C (50°F) during placement and for three days afterwards. For walls, leave forms in place for two days to enhance the heat of hydration. Cover slabs with insulating materials or straw covered with tarpaulins or polyethylene.

◆ Use a concrete mix with a low water content, adding plasticizers as necessary. Specify high early-strength concrete.

◆ Have the supplier provide heated concrete by using hot water and dry aggregates.

◆ If calcium chloride is used as an accelerator, limit the amount to less than 2 percent of the weight of the cement. Note that accelerators can increase the likelihood of shrinkage cracking. Calcium chloride must not be used in concrete that has metal inclusions. Non-chloride accelerators must not be used. Do not use calcium chloride in the excavation to melt ice.

◆ In Western Canada, builders often cast floor joists into foundation walls, making it easier to cover them with tarpaulins and heat them.

If heaters are used inside the building, be sure to provide adequate ventilation. Heaters will produce significant quantities of carbon monoxide, which can result in carbonation (dusting) on the surfaces of the concrete. As carbon monoxide is heavier than air, air should be exhausted from near the floor.

Cause

Inadequate hot weather precautions—above 30°C (86°F)

Excessively rapid drying of concrete in hot weather will reduce the strength of the concrete. Concrete, in hot weather, may flash-set during placement.

Solutions

Minimize moisture loss from the concrete.

◆ Dampen the subgrade and formwork before you pour the concrete.

◆ Have the supplier provide a suitable mix for hot weather placement. Reducing concrete temperatures and using set retarders may prove advantageous. Avoid delays in transportation to, and placement on, the site (discharge within an hour of mixing in hot weather). Place concrete early in the morning or in the evening. Protect concrete from rapid drying caused by direct sun and winds. Apply fog spray immediately after placement and before finishing. Cover with opaque polyethylene between finishing stages.

◆ Suppliers can calculate the correct amount of water to be added to the mix, based on the rate of water loss as influenced by temperature, relative humidity, wind speed, and concrete temperature.

PROBLEM
SHRINKAGE CRACKS

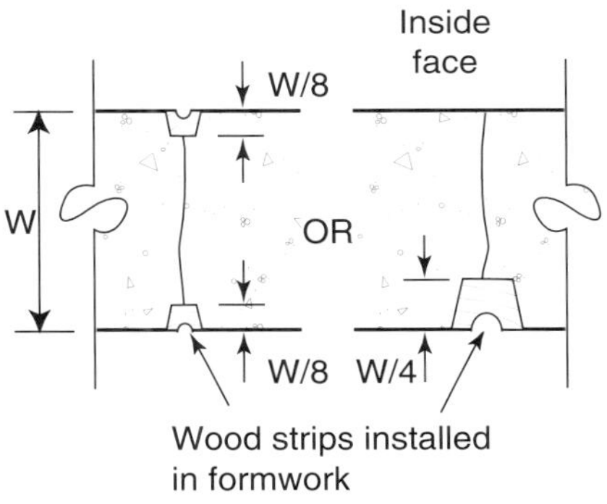

CAUSE

Normal drying of concrete

Shrinkage occurs when particles of cement and aggregate draw together to fill voids that appear when excess water evaporates from the concrete.

SOLUTIONS

Minimize the amount of shrinkage.

◆ Shrinkage can be minimized by

– not adding water on the construction site. Adding air entrainment or a super-plasticizer to the mix will improve workability and reduce the potential for shrinkage cracks;

– using the maximum allowable aggregate size;

– ensuring proper curing of concrete (moist-cure concrete surfaces for three days, and leave formwork on walls for a minimum of 24 hours at temperatures close to 13°C [56°F]); and

– adding fly ash to the concrete mix to slow the setting time.

FIGURE 9
VERTICAL CONTROL-JOINT DETAIL

W/8
Inside face
W
OR
W/8 W/4
Wood strips installed in formwork

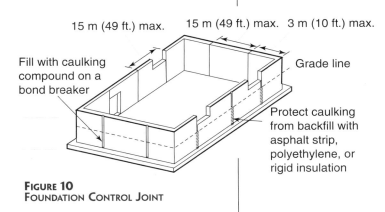

15 m (49 ft.) max. 15 m (49 ft.) max. 3 m (10 ft.) max.

Fill with caulking compound on a bond breaker

Grade line

Protect caulking from backfill with asphalt strip, polyethylene, or rigid insulation

FIGURE 10
FOUNDATION CONTROL JOINT

Use control joints to minimize random cracking and leakage. Control joints help you to predetermine where shrinkage cracking will occur: they intentionally weaken the slab or wall. The use of control joints can reduce foundation callbacks by 90 percent.

◆ To be effective, control joints must reduce the thickness of the wall by 25 percent. Attach bevelled wood strips to formwork or saw-cut immediately after forms are removed (see Figure 9).

◆ The NBC requires that control joints shall be provided in foundation walls more than 25 m (82 ft.) long, and at intervals of not more than 15 m (49 ft.) (see Figure 10).

◆ On the exterior, joints must be sealed with gun-grade, oil-based caulking applied over a bond breaker (see Figure 11). Sealant should be protected from the backfill soil with asphalt paper, heavy polyethylene, or rigid insulation installed to grade.

◆ Tool in control joints in floor slabs when you are finishing. Make saw-cuts 6 to 18 hours after placement, and space them at 4.5 to 6 m (15 to 20 ft.) for basements and 3.5 to 4.5 m (12 to 15 ft.) for garages. The depth of the control joints should be one quarter of the slab thickness.

Sealant in
control joint

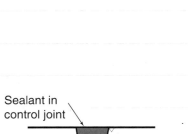

Crack closed

Crack opened – no bond breaker

Crack opened – with bond breaker

FIGURE 11
EFFECT OF A BOND BREAKER

PROBLEM
CRACKS IN FOUNDATIONS AND SLABS RESULTING FROM SETTLEMENT AND MOVEMENT

CAUSE

Differential movement

Foundation walls and basement slabs may be subjected to different pressures or conditions that cause movement. If it is not isolated, the movement of one component can result in the cracking of the other component.

SOLUTIONS

Provide isolation joints or a bond breaker between materials that might move relative to others.

◆ Separate the basement slab from the foundation wall with premoulded joint material, building paper, or expansion joint materials. The slab will be isolated from footings by polyethylene or other bond-breaking material, required as soil gas control by the NBC (see Figure 12).

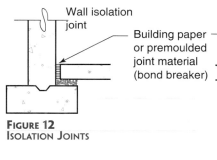
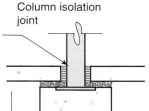

Wall isolation joint

Building paper or premoulded joint material (bond breaker)

Column isolation joint

FIGURE 12
ISOLATION JOINTS

◆ Separate the basement slab from the column with an isolation joint.

◆ Separate the basement foundation from the garage foundation with an isolation joint. The joint should continue up through any masonry cladding to protect against differential movement.

CAUSE

Differential movement and cracking of the garage slab

Greater settlement of garage slabs at their edges relative to the centre of the slab will result in cracking.

SOLUTIONS

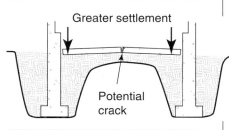

Greater settlement

Potential crack

FIGURE 13
GARAGE SLAB CRACKING

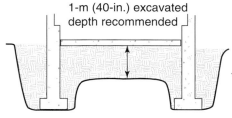

1-m (40-in.) excavated depth recommended

Ensure that granular fill is evenly distributed and compacted under the garage slab.

◆ Excavate to a minimum depth of 1 metre (40 in.) under the garage. Differential settlement can occur where the centre of the garage excavation is significantly higher than at the perimeter (see Figure 13).

◆ Compact granular fill to reduce the likelihood of differential settlement.

PROBLEM

CRACKS IN FOUNDATIONS AND SLABS RESULTING FROM SETTLEMENT AND MOVEMENT

CAUSE

Problem soils

Problem soils commonly encountered in Canada include peat and organic soils, soils in abandoned landfill sites, and clays (including normal, expansive, and sensitive clays).

SOLUTIONS

Modify designs to suit the specific soil conditions.

◆ When encountering poor soil conditions, continue to excavate until you reach stable soils, or perform soil tests to determine foundation design requirements.

◆ Peat or organic soils will settle as moisture is squeezed out of the soils. Flexible service connections will be required. To minimize settlement problems

   – replace shallow peat deposits with compacted granular fill;

   – use end-bearing or deep-friction piles;

   – use raft foundations; and

   – use wider, reinforced footings (see Figure 14).

◆ In normally consolidated clays (Windsor, Lake St. Clair, parts of northern Manitoba, Ontario, and Quebec), use piles to prevent long-term settlement.

◆ Swelling or expansive clays (as found in Manitoba, Saskatchewan and Alberta) will shrink or expand as they dry out or absorb water. To minimize problems, you can do the following:

   – reinforce foundation walls to act as grade beams, and use piles to support walls (at corners) and teleposts (see Figure 15);

   – employ a rigid foundation system consisting of reinforced walls and hollow-core floors to withstand differential settlement and twisting; and

   – use a suspended wooden floor rather than a basement slab to avoid uplift pressures on the basement floor.

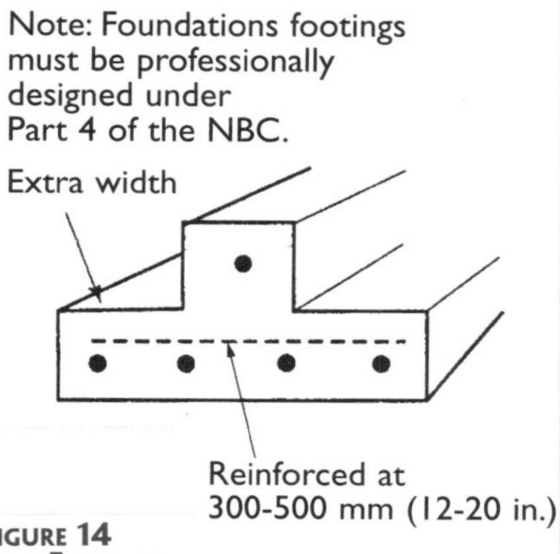

Note: Foundations footings must be professionally designed under Part 4 of the NBC.

Extra width

Reinforced at 300-500 mm (12-20 in.)

FIGURE 14
PEAT FOOTING

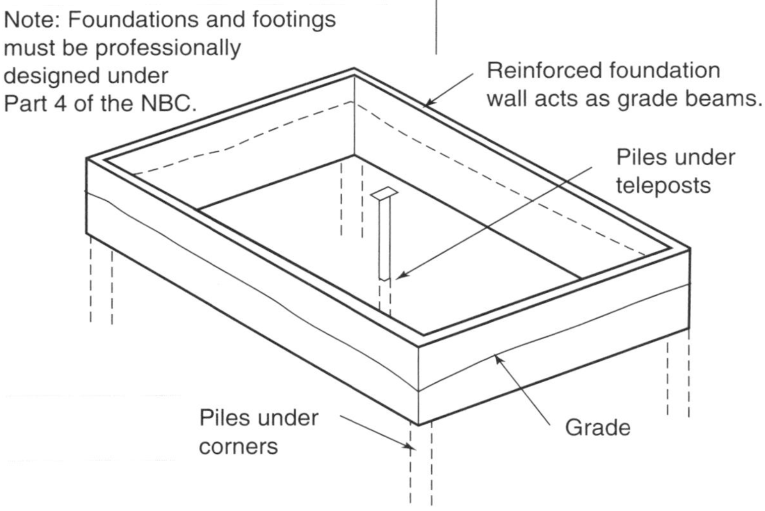

Note: Foundations and footings must be professionally designed under Part 4 of the NBC.

Reinforced foundation wall acts as grade beams.

Piles under teleposts

Piles under corners

Grade

FIGURE 15
REINFORCED FOUNDATION FOR EXPANSIVE CLAY SOILS

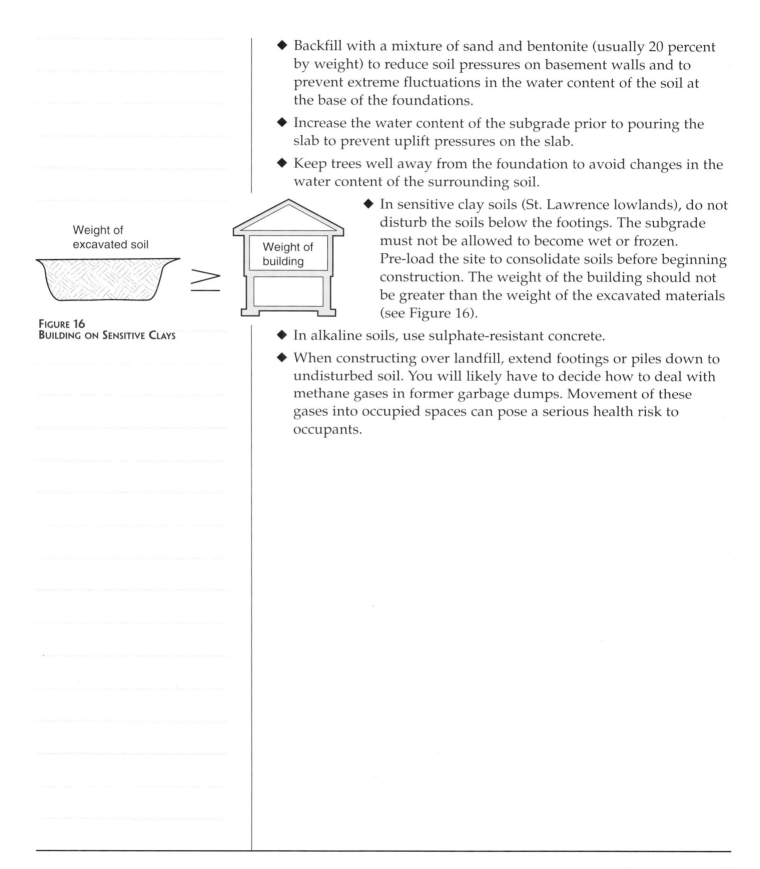

Weight of
excavated soil

FIGURE 16
BUILDING ON SENSITIVE CLAYS

Weight of
building

◆ Backfill with a mixture of sand and bentonite (usually 20 percent by weight) to reduce soil pressures on basement walls and to prevent extreme fluctuations in the water content of the soil at the base of the foundations.

◆ Increase the water content of the subgrade prior to pouring the slab to prevent uplift pressures on the slab.

◆ Keep trees well away from the foundation to avoid changes in the water content of the surrounding soil.

◆ In sensitive clay soils (St. Lawrence lowlands), do not disturb the soils below the footings. The subgrade must not be allowed to become wet or frozen. Pre-load the site to consolidate soils before beginning construction. The weight of the building should not be greater than the weight of the excavated materials (see Figure 16).

◆ In alkaline soils, use sulphate-resistant concrete.

◆ When constructing over landfill, extend footings or piles down to undisturbed soil. You will likely have to decide how to deal with methane gases in former garbage dumps. Movement of these gases into occupied spaces can pose a serious health risk to occupants.

PROBLEM

CRACKS IN FOUNDATIONS AND SLABS RESULTING FROM FROST HEAVING AND FREEZING

CAUSE

Footings not extending below the frostline

Most commonly, this problem occurs at garage frost walls and basement walk-outs where excavations may not be deep enough to get below the frostline.

SOLUTIONS

Ensure that all footings are located below the frostline or are protected by an insulated skirt.

◆ All footings, including those supporting garages and those below basement walk-outs, must be maintained below the depth of frost penetration. Information on the local depth of frost penetration is available through municipal building departments (see Figure 17).

◆ Have shallow footings professionally designed to minimize frost penetration. Use vertical and horizontal insulation to protect the footings (see Figure 18).

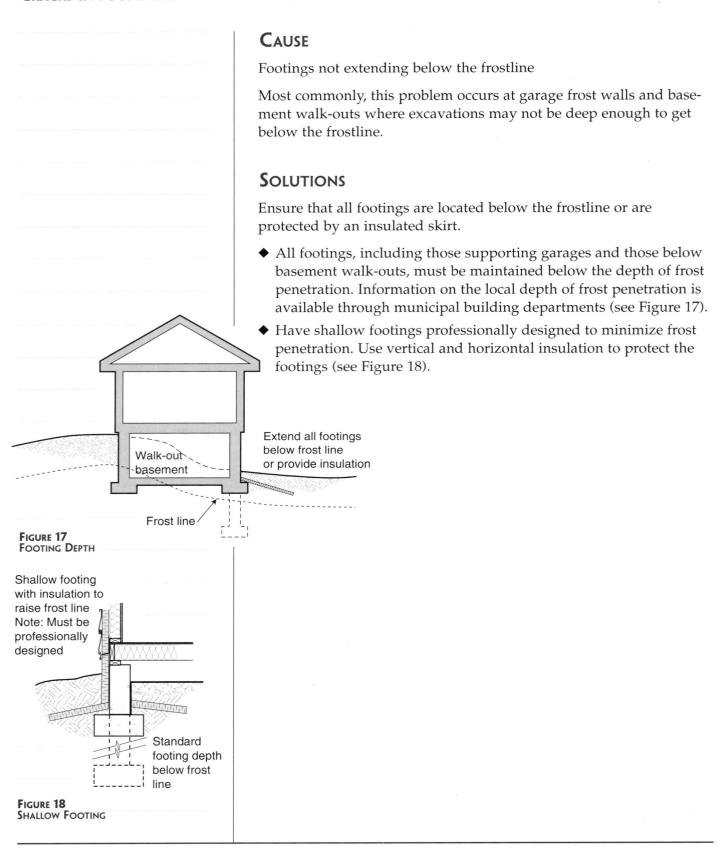

Extend all footings below frost line or provide insulation

Walk-out basement

Frost line

FIGURE 17
FOOTING DEPTH

Shallow footing with insulation to raise frost line Note: Must be professionally designed

Standard footing depth below frost line

FIGURE 18
SHALLOW FOOTING

Cause

Moisture in soil adhering to the foundation wall and the lifting foundation

This problem usually occurs at garage frost walls, which are not subjected to high enough interior heat to prevent it.

Isolate the wall from the moisture in the soil or minimize the likelihood of moisture in the soil that is in contact with the foundation wall.

◆ Keep frost-susceptible soils away from the foundation wall. Provide a capillary break between the soil and the foundation wall. Use free-draining backfill, free-draining insulation, or air-gap membrane products to isolate the foundation wall from the moisture-laden soils (see Figure 19).

◆ Install drainage tile to remove moisture from around the footings, or install a granular drainage layer over soil graded to a sump pit.

◆ Separate the garage and house foundations from the above-grade elements, using isolation joints to prevent stresses and defects related to differential movement.

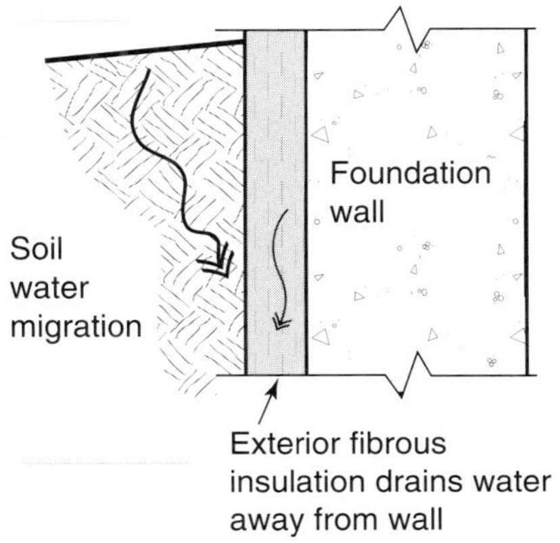

Soil water migration

Foundation wall

Exterior fibrous insulation drains water away from wall

FIGURE 19
DRAINAGE LAYER

PROBLEM
DETERIORATION FROM SALT ATTACK

CAUSE

Weak, permeable concrete

After several years of exposure to de-icing salts, some concrete will visibly deteriorate. Spalling and cracking are likely to occur as the salts permeate the concrete.

SOLUTIONS

Provide higher-strength concrete which is resistant to salt damage.

A comparison of municipal sidewalks with garage and driveway slabs will often show a significant difference in durability—the sidewalk concrete lasts longer and looks better. The better performance results from higher-strength concrete and better placement procedures.

◆ Use concrete with a higher-strength design mix (30-MPa [4 350-psi]), concrete with higher levels of air entrainment (5 to 8 percent), or sulphate-resistant concrete. Ensure proper curing of the slab.

◆ Do not overtrowel the slab. Overtrowelling (especially with a steel trowel) removes the entrained air and increases the water-cement ratio at the slab surface. Use a wood float and broomed finish to enhance durability.

◆ Seal control joints and saw-cuts in garage slabs with a flexible sealant to prevent the penetration into the slab of salts and of moisture that is prone to freeze–thaw cycles (see Figure 20).

◆ Allow at least 30 days of air drying before exposing the driveway and garage slabs to freeze–thaw cycles.

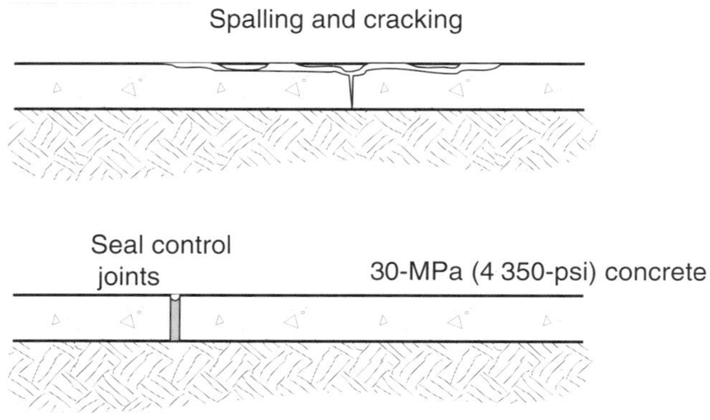

Spalling and cracking

Seal control joints

30-MPa (4 350-psi) concrete

FIGURE 20
MINIMIZING SALT DAMAGE

1.1.2 WATER LEAKAGE
P R O B L E M

WATER LEAKAGE THROUGH FOUNDATIONS

CAUSE

Inadequate site drainage

SOLUTIONS

Ensure that rainwater is diverted away from the foundation.

◆ While a 2 percent slope away from foundation walls is commonly specified, a 10 percent slope away from the wall for the first 2 m (8-in. slope in 6 ft., 6 in.) is recommended. This increase will ensure positive slope away from the building after the ground has settled around the foundation (see Figure 21).

◆ Locate downspouts around the perimeter of the building to ensure that rainwater is directed away from the building. Provide splash blocks to promote positive flows and to prevent erosion.

◆ On a sloping site, place the building at an angle to the slope to prevent the house from acting as a dam to natural run-off, or grade from the centre of the house to the corners to direct water away from the building (see Figure 22). Provide swales to promote drainage.

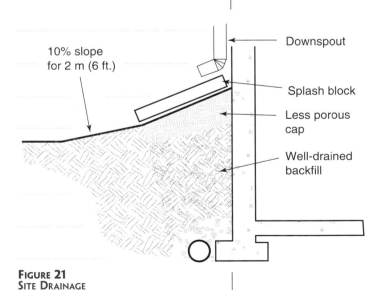

FIGURE 21
SITE DRAINAGE

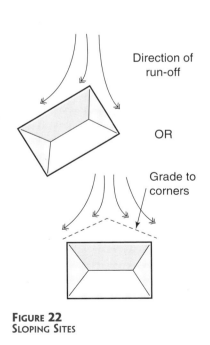

FIGURE 22
SLOPING SITES

PROBLEM
WATER LEAKAGE THROUGH FOUNDATIONS

CAUSE

Improperly installed drainage tile

Drainage tile will not perform as intended when it is not properly sloped, when it becomes clogged, or when it does not drain water away from the site.

SOLUTIONS

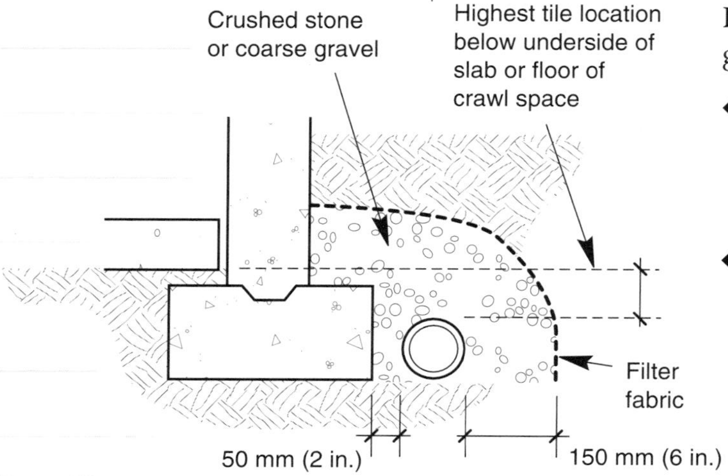

Ensure correct installation of drainage tile or a granular drainage layer.

◆ Leave clearance of 35 to 50 mm (1-1/2 to 2 in.) between the tile and the footing to reduce clogging in this area and to increase the drainage area.

◆ Set the tile at the bottom of the footing on undisturbed soil or compacted soil. Ensure that the entire drain tile is located below the underside of the basement slab or floor of the crawl space. Cover the drain tile with a minimum of 150 mm (6 in.) of granular material. To prevent the accumulation of silt and fines in the tile, use a filter fabric or glass fibre batt to cover the granular material or the tile itself (see Figure 23).

◆ Ensure that drainage from window wells is connected to drainage tiles. Prevent water from accumulating at the junction of the footing and the foundation wall. Provide a "French drain," a vertical gravel- or drainage-material-filled weeper (see Figure 24).

◆ Install granular material (clean, containing not more than 10 percent material that will pass through a 4-mm [1/6-in.] sieve) to a depth of 125 mm (5 in.) beneath the building, extending not less than 300 mm (12 in.) beyond the outside edge of the footings. The bottom of the excavation using the granular drainage layer must be sloped so that the entire area is drained to a sump. Sump pits should be at least 300 mm (12 in.) below the level of the floor slab to ensure adequate drainage.

Crushed stone or coarse gravel

Highest tile location below underside of slab or floor of crawl space

Filter fabric

50 mm (2 in.) 150 mm (6 in.)

FIGURE 23
WEEPING-TILE DETAIL

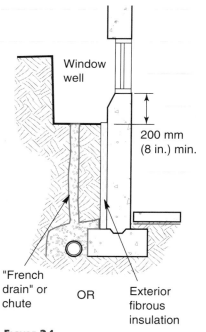

Window well

200 mm (8 in.) min.

"French drain" or chute OR Exterior fibrous insulation

FIGURE 24
WINDOW-WELL DRAINAGE

PROBLEM
WATER LEAKAGE THROUGH FOUNDATIONS

CAUSE

Leakage through form-tie holes

When forms are stripped, form-tie paths through the foundation wall can provide a ready path for water entry when the wall is not adequately sealed.

SOLUTIONS

Waterproof form-tie holes and other repaired areas before applying damp-proofing.

◆ Prevent voids below form-ties with good placement and consolidation techniques.

◆ Cut back tie-holes and other repaired areas by a minimum of 15 mm (5/8 in.) (see Figure 25).

   ◆ Patch all holes before applying damp-proofing. Use rapid-set grout, stiff Portland cement mortar, or mastics that are designed to bond with green concrete (see Figure 26).

   ◆ Ensure that patches are installed flush to the foundation wall to prevent damage during backfill.

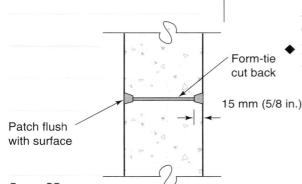

Form-tie cut back

15 mm (5/8 in.)

Patch flush with surface

FIGURE 25
FORM-TIE PATCHING

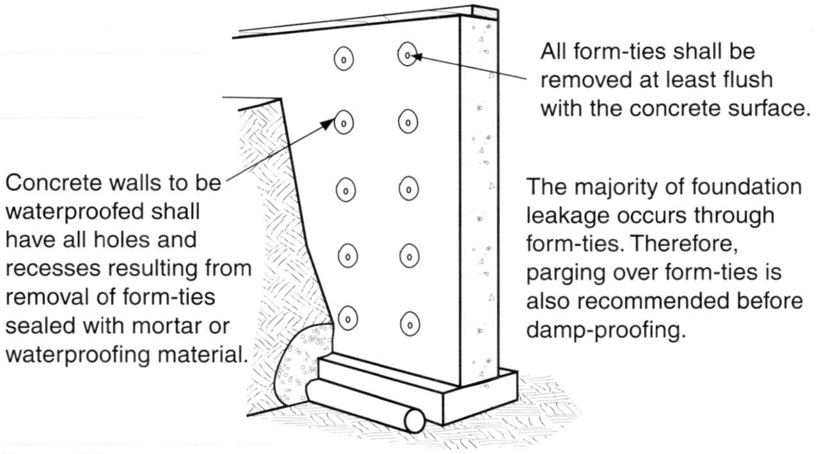

Concrete walls to be waterproofed shall have all holes and recesses resulting from removal of form-ties sealed with mortar or waterproofing material.

All form-ties shall be removed at least flush with the concrete surface.

The majority of foundation leakage occurs through form-ties. Therefore, parging over form-ties is also recommended before damp-proofing.

FIGURE 26
FORM-TIE PATCHING

PROBLEM

CONDENSATION ON INTERIOR OF FOUNDATION WALLS

CAUSE

Inadequate damp-proofing

While some condensation on foundation walls in spring and summer can result from interior humid air contacting cooler surfaces, excessive condensation or moisture in basements is often the result of the movement of soil moisture through the foundation wall and floor slab. Builders should not confuse the role of damp-proofing with that of waterproofing. Damp-proofing is intended to prevent the flow of water vapour in the soil. It is not intended to prevent water leakage through cracks and holes in the wall.

SOLUTIONS

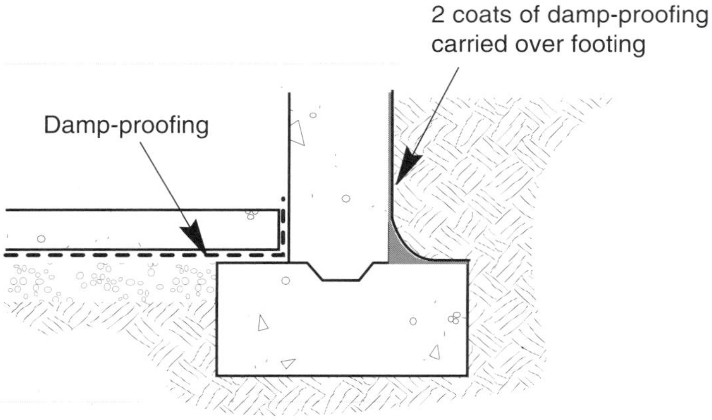

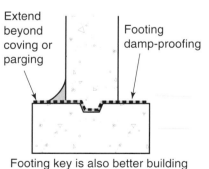

2 coats of damp-proofing carried over footing

Damp-proofing

FIGURE 27
DAMP-PROOFING FOUNDATION WALLS AND SLABS

Extend beyond coving or parging

Footing damp-proofing

Footing key is also better building practice, improving lateral support

FIGURE 28
CONTROLLING CAPILLARY WATER

Ensure that damp-proofing is effectively installed on foundation walls and under floor slabs.

◆ Brush walls to remove dirt, dust, oils, and scale before you apply damp-proofing materials.

◆ Spray or roll on two coats of damp-proofing at right angles to grade level on the exterior. The damp-proofing should be carried over the top of the footing. Ensure that the final coat of damp-proofing is firm before you backfill (see Figure 27).

◆ Consider the use of exterior membrane materials which serve as effective replacements for damp-proof coatings.

◆ Provide damp-proofing under floor slabs to prevent moisture from seeping through slabs. Polyethylene (0.15 mm [6 mil]) or Type S roll roofing with joints lapped no less than 100 mm (4 in.) are acceptable options.

◆ To prevent wicking of soil moisture up through the footing to the foundation wall, install damp-proofing materials over the footing before you pour the wall. Ensure that adequate bonding is maintained between the wall and the footing key (see Figure 28).

PROBLEM
HUMID, DAMP, OR MUSTY BASEMENT OR CRAWL SPACE

CAUSE

Entry of soil vapour through cracks in the floor slab or foundation walls

Airborne vapour transfer can occur through both foundation walls and basement slabs. Air can move through porous soils or granular fill into buildings through cracks in walls and slabs, and through weeping tile systems into houses, carrying soil moisture into the occupied spaces. Radon and other soil gases can also be carried into houses along these unsealed air paths.

SOLUTIONS

Ensure that foundations, slabs, and all connections are airtight.

◆ Minimize cracking in floor slabs and foundation walls by using good mixing, placement, and curing techniques.

  ◆ Seal the joint between the floor slab and the foundation wall with a durable caulking—either a single-component urethane or a single-component silicone—or extend polyethylene from below the slab-on-ground up the wall (see Figure 29).

  ◆ Make sure that air is not leaking into the building around the floor drains. Install a trap primer to ensure that the trap at the floor drain never dries out (see Figure 30).

  ◆ Ensure an effective seal around sumps, using a tight-fitting cover.

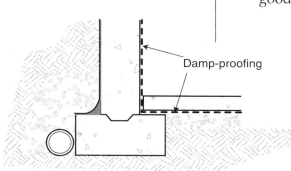

Damp-proofing

FIGURE 29
EXTENDING POLYETHYLENE FROM BELOW FLOOR SLAB

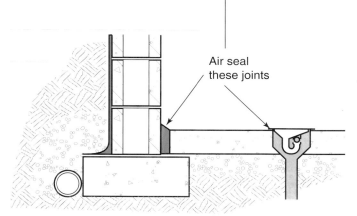

Air seal these joints

FIGURE 30
POTENTIAL SOURCES OF AIR LEAKAGE

CAUSE

Moisture in crawl spaces

Exposed soils can be a significant source of moisture in houses with crawl spaces. Without moisture protection and suitable ventilation, crawl spaces are likely to be damp, humid, and unhealthy areas.

SOLUTIONS

Install a moisture barrier and suitable ventilation.

◆ Cover soil in unheated crawl spaces with either 100 mm (4 in.) of 15-MPa (2 175-psi) concrete, Type S roll roofing or 0.10-mm (4-mil) polyethylene. Joints in sheet materials should be lapped a minimum of 100 mm (4 in.), and should be weighted down with sand or another suitable ballast material.

◆ Natural ventilation should be supplied for unheated crawl spaces during the summer and fall by a vent area of not less than 0.1 m² for every 50 m² (1 sq. ft./500 sq. ft.) of floor area, evenly distributed on opposite sides of the crawl space to promote cross ventilation. Vents shall be screened to prevent the entry of snow, rain, and insects (see Figure 31).

◆ Insulate and vent heated crawl spaces to the adjacent basement space. Ground cover in heated crawl spaces must be not less than 0.15-mm (6-mil) polyethylene conforming to CAN-CGSB-51.34-M, lapped a minimum of 300 mm (12 in.), and either weighted down with sand or covered with a concrete skim coat of not less than 50 mm (2 in.) (see Figure 32).

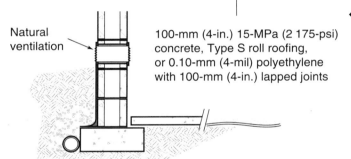

Natural ventilation

100-mm (4-in.) 15-MPa (2 175-psi) concrete, Type S roll roofing, or 0.10-mm (4-mil) polyethylene with 100-mm (4-in.) lapped joints

FIGURE 31
REDUCING MOISTURE IN CRAWL SPACES

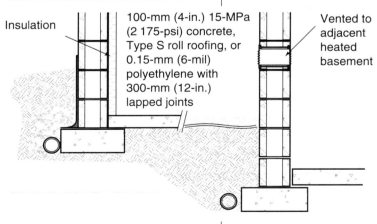

Insulation

100-mm (4-in.) 15-MPa (2 175-psi) concrete, Type S roll roofing, or 0.15-mm (6-mil) polyethylene with 300-mm (12-in.) lapped joints

Vented to adjacent heated basement

FIGURE 32
REDUCING MOISTURE IN CRAWL SPACES

PROBLEM
MOISTURE DAMAGE TO INTERIOR INSULATED FOUNDATION WALLS

CAUSE

Air leakage behind insulation

When interior insulation is applied to foundation walls, the surface temperature of the walls will decrease. When warmer humid air in the basement passes over the foundation walls, moisture in the air will condense out—sometimes resulting in puddling or staining under and out from the insulated wall section.

SOLUTIONS

Ensure that interior frame walls are air-sealed at the base and top to minimize air leakage and air circulation behind the insulated cavities.

◆ Install a moisture barrier/damp-proofing on the interior face of the foundation wall to protect wood framing and insulation from moisture in the concrete. The barrier should extend from the base of the foundation wall to the level of the exterior grade (see Figure 33). Any membranes or coatings applied above grade must have a permeability of not less than 170 ng/Pa•s•m^2 (2.95 grain/ft^{2}hr [in.Hg]).

◆ When framing interior walls, use sill gasket material (instead of polyethylene or building paper) under the bottom plate to reduce air leakage between the wood and concrete, or seal the drywall to the concrete at the base of a finished wall.

◆ Install an effective air barrier system, using either polyethylene (0.15 mm [6 mil]) or the airtight drywall approach (ADA) to prevent air leakage. Penetrations through the air barrier (service entrances, electrical outlets, furnace vents, ventilation exhaust and intake ducting, etc.) must be carefully sealed to prevent air leakage.

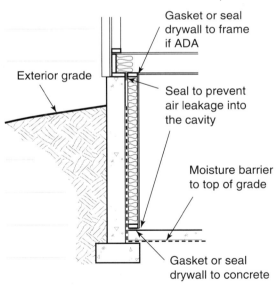

Gasket or seal drywall to frame if ADA

Exterior grade

Seal to prevent air leakage into the cavity

Moisture barrier to top of grade

Gasket or seal drywall to concrete

FIGURE 33
PROTECTING WOOD FRAMING AND INSULATION

PROBLEM
CREEP AND MOVEMENT OF EXTERIOR FOUNDATION INSULATION ABOVE GRADE

CAUSE

Frost adhesion

When not properly installed, exterior insulation can move as affected by soil pressures. Frost adhesion can raise exterior insulation, and soil settlement can lower the insulation relative to the above-grade elements of the cladding.

SOLUTIONS

Prevent movement caused by frost adhesion.

◆ Minimize moisture in the surrounding soil using free-draining fill, or free-draining insulation materials. Where moisture content in the soils adjacent to the insulation is low, lensing and adhesion is unlikely to occur.

◆ Ensure that insulation materials are adequately fastened to the foundation and capped at the top of the insulation to restrict upward movement. Mechanically fastened insulation is preferable to mastic-applied approaches (see Figure 34).

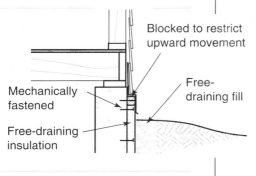

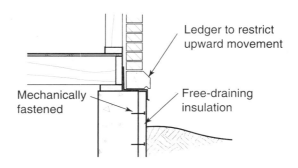

FIGURE 34
FASTENING OF INSULATION MATERIALS

CAUSE

Soil settlement around foundation

As soils settle, they can pull rigid exterior insulation down the wall if proper installation procedures have not been followed.

SOLUTIONS

Minimize soil settlement.

◆ Ensure rainwater drains away from the building, using proper grading, splash-block rainwater-leaders, and a sloped clay cap.

◆ Ensure proper compaction of backfill/granular fill around the foundation.

Use proper installation techniques.

◆ Ensure that exterior insulation rests directly on the footing to minimize slippage. When using free-draining insulation materials, ensure that draining water has direct access to the weeping-tile system (see Figure 35).

◆ Mechanically fasten the exterior insulation to the foundation wall.

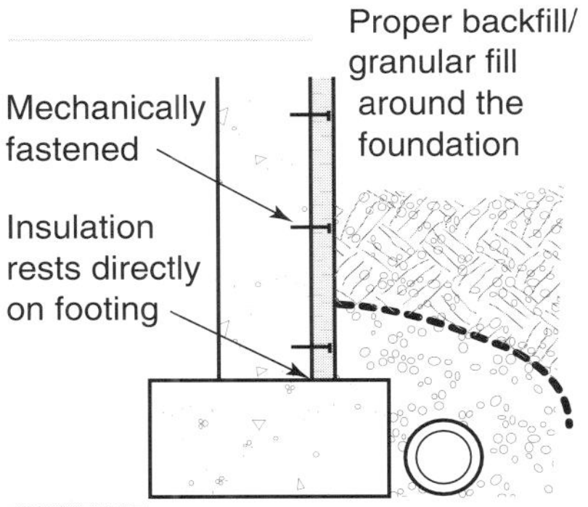

Mechanically fastened

Insulation rests directly on footing

Proper backfill/ granular fill around the foundation

FIGURE 35
EXTERIOR FOUNDATION INSULATION

Section 1.2 Slabs-on-ground
INTRODUCTION

Slab-on-ground house construction is not common in Canada. This is mainly due to market demands for basement space and building industry belief that the depth of frost penetration (and thus the required depth of footings) in much of Canada warrants the construction of full basements.

These perceptions are gradually changing as a result of an increasing demand for barrier-free housing for persons with disabilities and the elderly. For many of these people, basements are not necessarily a desirable feature.

Secondly, the building industry increasingly understands that slab-on-ground construction can be an economical construction technique suitable for most parts of the country, either in conjunction with frost-protected shallow foundation walls or with thickened slab edges. Structural "floating" slabs can also represent a viable alternative for construction in areas with unstable problem soils.

Where slab-on-ground construction supports building loads, design must conform to Part 4 of the NBC.

1.2.1 STRUCTURAL DETERIORATION AND DAMAGE
PROBLEM
CRACKING OF SLAB

CAUSE

Differential or uneven settlement

Differential or uneven settlement is caused by variations in the subgrade. When loaded, the slab will tend to bridge over soft spots (such as underground utilities where soil hasn't been adequately compacted) and rest on hard spots (such as rocks or denser soil). This differential settlement often results in cracking (see Figure 36).

SOLUTIONS

Ensure that the subgrade is completely uniform in firmness, grade level, and dampness.

◆ Remove all topsoil and organic materials to expose the natural ground. The strength of the soil is a function of the degree of its compaction and its moisture content.

◆ The boundaries of the compacted area should be extended 1.5 to 3.0 m (5 to 10 ft.) beyond the perimeter of the slab (see Figure 37). Compact the area around the slab-on-ground, and slope it to promote drainage away from the slab.

◆ Backfill soil used around service trenches should be similar to the soils surrounding the utility trench. Compact it in layers to duplicate the compaction and moisture conditions of the adjacent soil.

◆ After compacting the subgrade, install granular fill, and compact it across the entire area. A minimum of 100 mm (4 in.) of coarse, clean, granular fill is required beneath the slab (see Figure 38).

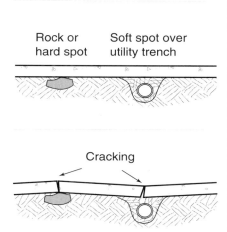

Rock or hard spot — Soft spot over utility trench

Cracking

FIGURE 36
UNEVEN SETTLEMENT

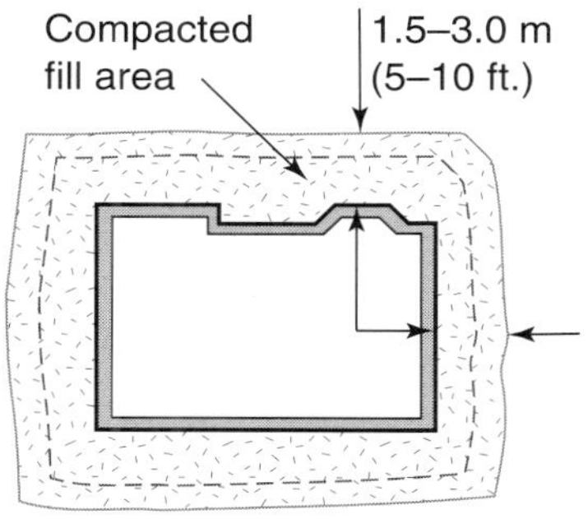

Compacted fill area — 1.5–3.0 m (5–10 ft.)

FIGURE 37
SUBGRADE COMPACTION

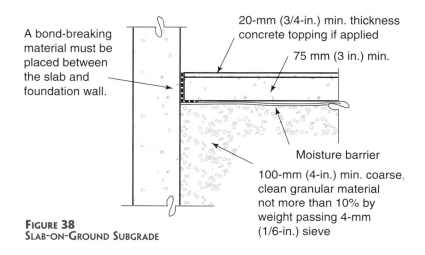

A bond-breaking material must be placed between the slab and foundation wall.

20-mm (3/4-in.) min. thickness concrete topping if applied

75 mm (3 in.) min.

Moisture barrier

100-mm (4-in.) min. coarse, clean granular material not more than 10% by weight passing 4-mm (1/6-in.) sieve

FIGURE 38
SLAB-ON-GROUND SUBGRADE

PROBLEM
CRACKING OF SLAB

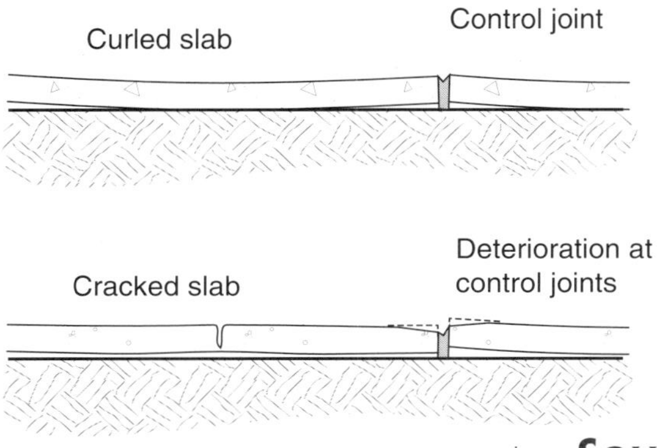

Curled slab   Control joint

Cracked slab   Deterioration at control joints

FIGURE 39
SLAB CURLING

CAUSE

Curling of the slab

As new concrete dries, it shrinks or shortens in all directions. In the case of concrete slabs-on-ground, the top surface of the slab is prone to shrink and dry more rapidly than the bottom surface. The tensile stresses created in the top of the slab and loads on the unsupported corners can cause the concrete to crack. While in most cases the effect is unnoticeable, in extreme circumstances, bumps, spalling, and cracking can result (see Figure 39).

SOLUTIONS

Minimize shrinkage of the concrete.

◆ Thicker slabs will tend to curl less than thinner slabs.

◆ Provide control joints in areas—such as penetrations—where cracking is likely to occur.

CAUSE

Inadequate structural strength of slab

Cracking will result where the structural strength of the slab cannot support the applied loads. The *Portland Cement Association* recommends control joints be located at intervals of 5 to 7 m (16 to 23 ft.) in both directions.

SOLUTIONS

Ensure that the slab is adequately designed.

◆ Section 9.16 of the NBC states requirements for non-load-bearing slabs-on-ground. When slabs-on-ground are intended as a structural element of the building, Part 4 of the NBC ("Structural Design") applies, requiring professional design by an architect or structural engineer skilled in the work concerned.

◆ Concrete used in slab-on-ground construction should have a minimum strength of 30 MPa (4 350 psi).

PROBLEM
CRACKING OF SLAB

CAUSE

Frost heave

Frost heave can occur where moisture in the soil beneath the slab-on-ground freezes, expands, and exerts vertical and horizontal pressures on the slab. As a general rule, frost heaving will occur at the perimeter of the slab where frost penetration is more significant. Heaving can result in structural defects and damage to the slab and the supported structure.

SOLUTIONS

Prevent soil below the slab from freezing.

◆ Never pour concrete on a frozen subgrade. Frozen soil is unstable and may settle unevenly, causing the slab to stress and crack.

◆ Keep moisture out of the materials that come in contact with the slab.

◆ Provide heat in the house during construction to prevent freezing of the soil below the slab.

◆ Provide skirt insulation around the perimeter of the foundation. The effects of skirt insulation on the pattern of isotherms in the soil around a slab-on-ground are illustrated in Figure 40.

◆ Insulating vertically and horizontally out from the slab perimeter with an appropriate amount of rigid insulation can maintain soil temperatures above the freezing point in most parts of Canada. Insulation at corners of the slab will need to project further to accommodate higher levels of heat transfer. Table 1 provides guidance on the amount of, and depth of, insulation required in different climatic areas. Specific amounts and location may need to be engineered. The table assumes the use of moisture-resistant plastic foam insulation, such as extruded polystyrene.

◆ Ensure that any perimeter insulation extending over the slab above grade is protected with parging, flashing, or another rigid material (metal, or pressure-treated plywood).

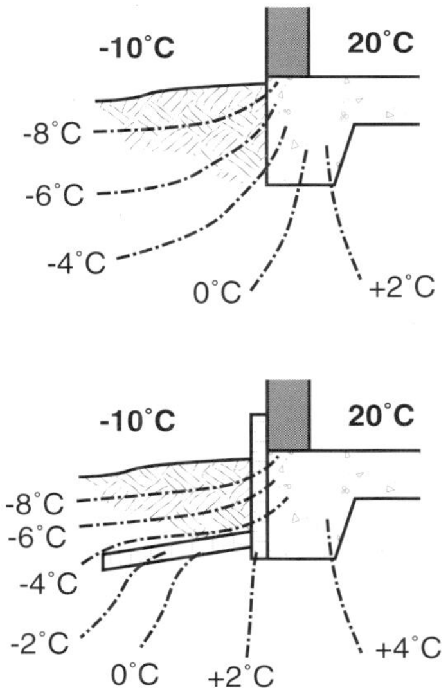

FIGURE 40
EFFECTS OF SKIRT INSULATION

Climate	Walls	Corners
Mild winters (coastal B.C., Southern Ontario)	50 mm (2 in.) extending outward 250 mm (10 in.)	50 mm (2 in.) extending outward 500 mm (20 in.) for 1.0 m (40 in.)
Moderate winters (Ontario, Québec, Atlantic Provinces)	50 mm (2 in.) extending outward 500 mm (20 in.)	75 mm (3 in.) extending outward 750 mm (30 in.) for 1.5 m (60 in.)
Severe winters (Prairies)	50 mm (2 in.) extending outward 750 mm (30 in.)	75 mm (3 in.) extending outward 1.0 m (40 in.) for 1.5 m (60 in.)

Table 1
Suggested Horizontal Perimeter Insulation for Shallow Foundations

1.2.2 WATER LEAKAGE

PROBLEM

DAMP OR WET FLOOR SLAB

CAUSE

Moisture migration up through the slab

SOLUTIONS

Provide a capillary break and appropriate resistance to moisture diffusion.

◆ Ensure good site drainage away from the slab.

◆ Provide a minimum of 100 mm (4 in.) of coarse, clean, granular fill below the slab-on-ground. This base will restrict capillary wicking of soil moisture and allow for depressurization below the slab to remove soil gases in areas where they might pose a problem.

◆ Provide a moisture barrier under the floor slabs to prevent moisture movement through the slabs. Polyethylene (0.15 mm [6 mil]) is commonly used.

1.2.3 INSULATION

PROBLEM

COLD FLOORS

CAUSE

Heat loss from the slab

To maintain appropriate soil temperatures below the slab, heat flow through the slabs-on-ground is required. Increasing the amount of perimeter insulation will increase soil temperatures below the slab, thus reducing heat loss. Caution: A minor difference between the temperature of the slab and that of the human body will be noticeable, so the more this difference is reduced, the better.

SOLUTIONS

Minimize direct contact with the slab, or warm the slab.

◆ Install carpeting or a false floor to minimize contact with the cooler surface temperature of the slab (see Figure 41).

◆ Provide radiant heating of the slab. This will improve comfort, but the higher rates of heat loss to the surrounding soils will increase heating costs. Typically in radiant heating, hot water is circulated in 12- to 19-mm (1/2- to 3/4-in.) polybutylene piping, spaced at 300 to 450 mm (12 to 18 in.) under (or embedded in) the slab (see Figure 42).

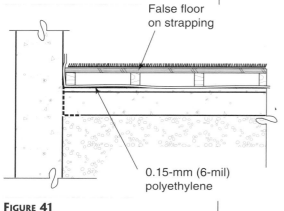

False floor on strapping

0.15-mm (6-mil) polyethylene

FIGURE 41
FALSE FLOOR

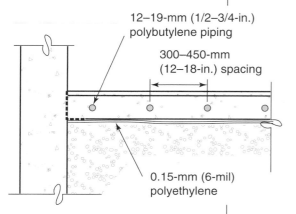

12–19-mm (1/2–3/4-in.) polybutylene piping

300–450-mm (12–18-in.) spacing

0.15-mm (6-mil) polyethylene

FIGURE 42
RADIANT HEATING OF SLAB-ON-GROUND

Section 1.3 Preserved-Wood Foundations

INTRODUCTION

Preserved-wood foundations (PWFs) have been growing in popularity throughout Canada, presenting an attractive alternative to masonry and concrete foundations in many markets. Although these foundations have been used in houses since the early 1960s, the widespread adoption of PWFs has been more recent, dating from the mid-1970s. By the mid-1990s, more than 100,000 PWFs had been constructed across the country.

Based on buried-stake tests, on accelerated weatherization tests, and on inspections of test foundations, a 75-year service life is predicted for PWFs.

Builders of PWF basements often claim the following advantages:

◆ Basements can be easily finished and insulated without additional framing or strapping.

◆ As a general rule, high levels of insulation can be accommodated, resulting in improved energy efficiency and greater comfort.

◆ Thanks to their adaptability to winter conditions and wet weather, their use reduces construction times.

◆ They allow for easier coordination and scheduling of trades.

◆ In areas where ready-mixed concrete is not easily available, PWFs are a favourable alternative to hand mixing concrete.

◆ PWF sections can be prefabricated and moved to the site for rapid installation.

At the same time, several limitations of PWFs have been noted:

◆ PWF construction requires stricter design and construction supervision to ensure that sufficient structural strength and durability is achieved.

◆ PWF construction requires engineered design and certification where the following conditions established in CAN/CSA 3-S406-M92 are exceeded:

- minimum soil bearing capacity: 75 MPa (1 600 psi);

- maximum soil pressure: 4.7 kPa (100 psf);

- maximum ground snow load: 3 kPa (65 psf); and

- maximum clear span: 5 m (16 ft., 8 in.).

(Note: Some local authorities may require professional designs for all PWFs.)

◆ Failures of PWFs in problem soil areas where design or construction was incorrect resulted in expensive repair work.

The Canadian Standards Association and the Canadian Wood Council provide design tables and specific detailing of construction using PWFs. Houses constructed with PWFs must be built in accordance with CAN/CSA 3-S406.

1.3.1 STRUCTURAL DETERIORATION AND DAMAGE
PROBLEM

PRESSURES ON FOUNDATIONS

CAUSE

Problem soils

The two factors affecting soil pressures on foundation walls are the type of soil and the amount of hydrostatic pressure. Hydrostatic pressures can be controlled in most cases through the adoption of good drainage principles.

SOLUTIONS

◆ The NBC requires that PWFs constructed under Part 9 must be supported on soils with bearing pressures of not less than 75 kPa (1500 psf).

◆ If problem soil is suspected, have soil tests taken to determine the permeability of the soil and the height of the water table.

◆ For swelling clays, backfill with porous material to within 300 mm (12 in.) of grade and 900 mm (3 ft.) out from the wall (see Figure 43). Some pressures may still be transmitted to the wall through the backfill once it has become consolidated. Compressible exterior insulation may provide an additional measure of safety.

◆ Backfill silty, frost-susceptible soils with granular material. This will prevent spring run-off from collecting in the backfill material and then freezing and exerting pressure against the foundation walls.

◆ Replace poorly draining soils whose vertical permeability is less than 0.001 cm/s (0.002 ft./min)—such as silty sands or fines—with granular backfill, and consider using a filter fabric to prevent the backfill from silting up.

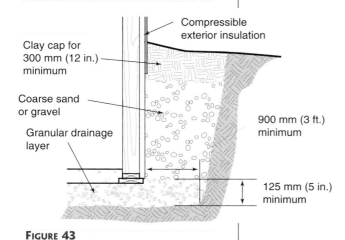

Compressible exterior insulation

Clay cap for 300 mm (12 in.) minimum

Coarse sand or gravel

Granular drainage layer

900 mm (3 ft.) minimum

125 mm (5 in.) minimum

FIGURE 43
BACKFILL FOR PROBLEM SOILS

- Avoid building with PWFs where there is a high water table. Establish the top of the granular drainage layer at least 750 mm (2 ft., 6 in.) above the typical water table.

- Where there is a risk of a temporary build-up of hydrostatic pressures (during heavy rains for example), provide a drainage layer deeper than the required 125 mm (5 in.).

- Using CSA design tables, determine the correct width of the footing plate based on number of storeys, type of basement floor, and type of exterior finish. Typically, footing plates will be one size larger than wall plates.

- Offset joints in footing plates and wall plates.

- Provide additional framing support for stepped footings (see Figure 44).

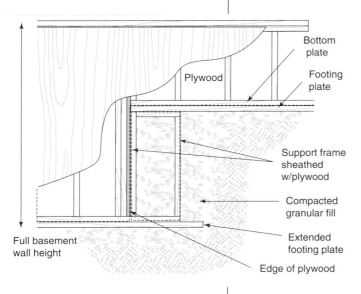

FIGURE 44
STEPPED FOOTING (ELEVATION)

PROBLEM
DIFFERENTIAL SETTLEMENT

CAUSE

Lack of adequate bearing for columns

SOLUTIONS

◆ For interior columns, place a steel plate on a crib of two layers of PWF members that are positioned on edge on undisturbed soil or on a levelling bed of sand (see Figure 45). Determine correct sizes from CSA-approved design tables, based on the number of storeys, beam span, and building width.

◆ Nail column footings sufficiently to prevent break-up when they are dropped into the excavation.

◆ Avoid splitting members in built-up column footings. Provide only a single row of nails, and keep nails at least 100 mm (4 in.) away from the ends.

◆ Support beams with beam pockets built up of PWF members, and provide additional crib footings below the footing plate (see Figure 46).

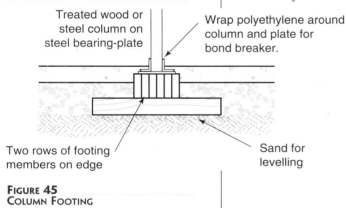

Treated wood or steel column on steel bearing-plate

Wrap polyethylene around column and plate for bond breaker.

Two rows of footing members on edge

Sand for levelling

FIGURE 45
COLUMN FOOTING

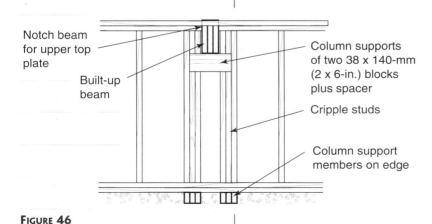

Notch beam for upper top plate

Built-up beam

Column supports of two 38 x 140-mm (2 x 6-in.) blocks plus spacer

Cripple studs

Column support members on edge

FIGURE 46
BEAM POCKET

PROBLEM
DIFFERENTIAL SETTLEMENT

CAUSE

Lack of support for masonry veneer

SOLUTIONS

◆ To support masonry veneer, provide a sufficiently wide foundation wall, or construct a separate 38 x 89-mm (2 x 4-in.) knee wall toe-nailed in line with the main wall and positioned on the exterior of the sheathing and moisture barrier (see Figure 47).

◆ Provide treated doubled top plates below brick veneer.

◆ For knee walls, tie composite footings together with PWF plywood. Carry knee-wall sheathing at least 300 mm (12 in.) below grade. The stud spaces below this can be backfilled as desired.

◆ Do not extend brick veneer higher than two storeys. The CSA standard allows a maximum height of 5.5 m (18 ft.) of brick.

Note: Some local authorities may not accept wood-frame support for masonry veneer.

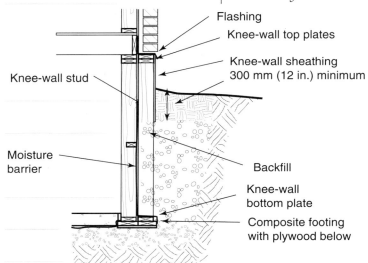

Flashing
Knee-wall top plates
Knee-wall sheathing
300 mm (12 in.) minimum
Knee-wall stud
Moisture barrier
Backfill
Knee-wall bottom plate
Composite footing with plywood below

FIGURE 47
MASONRY VENEER ON KNEE WALL

PROBLEM
DEFLECTION FROM SOIL PRESSURE

CAUSE

Understrength materials and assemblies

Foundation walls need to resist continuous loads from the soil, occasional hydrostatic pressure, fluctuating water tables, and the house above. PWFs require additional lateral support at both the base and top of the foundation walls to allow them to resist these pressures (see Figure 48).

SOLUTIONS

◆ Determine the correct stud size and spacing according to CSA design tables, based on vertical loading, type of basement floor and height of backfill; 38 x 140 mm (2 x 6 in.) and 38 x 184 mm (2 x 8 in.) studs are used in most Canadian applications.

◆ Determine the correct plywood thickness from CSA design tables, based on stud spacing, backfill heights and plywood alignment; 12.5 mm and 15.5 mm (1/2 in. and 5/8 in.) are used in most Canadian applications.

◆ For greater strength, apply plywood with the face grain perpendicular to the studs. If plywood is applied parallel, CSA design tables may require thicker sheets.

◆ Provide blocking for horizontal plywood joints (see Figure 49).

◆ Do not cut blocking or studs for ductwork or piping.

◆ Avoid using studs with large edge-knots. These members are better used for plates or blocking. If you must use them, place the studs so that the edge-knot faces the plywood sheathing.

Nails are better than staples for racking resistance. If staples are used, space them more closely than nails.

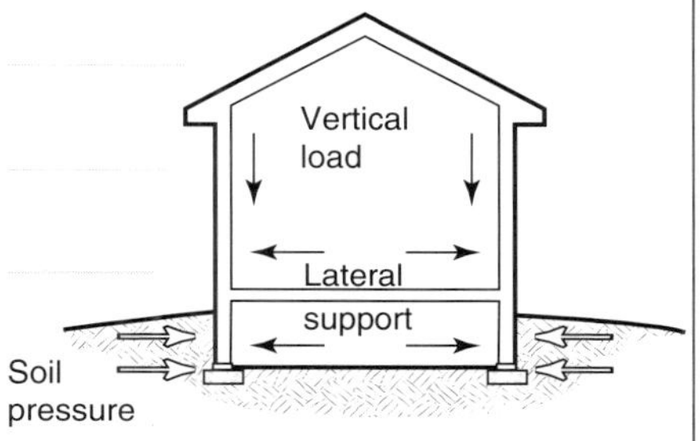

FIGURE 48
LATERAL SUPPORT

Vertical load

Lateral support

Soil pressure

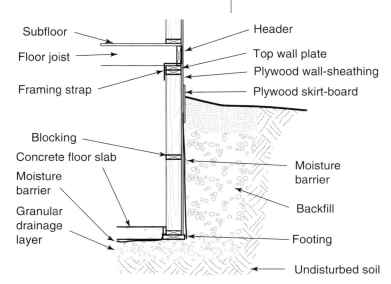

FIGURE 49
TYPICAL WALL SECTION

Subfloor
Floor joist
Framing strap
Blocking
Concrete floor slab
Moisture barrier
Granular drainage layer

Header
Top wall plate
Plywood wall-sheathing
Plywood skirt-board
Moisture barrier
Backfill
Footing
Undisturbed soil

PROBLEM
DEFLECTION FROM SOIL PRESSURE

CAUSE

Lack of lateral support at the base of the wall

SOLUTIONS

Acceptable basement floor systems include concrete slabs, wood sleepers, and suspended wood frames.

◆ For a concrete floor slab, ensure that there is at least 25 mm (1 in.) of concrete bearing against the wall studs. Pour concrete against a PWF screed board (see Figure 50).

◆ For a wood sleeper floor, toe-nail joists in line with the studs, double the joists where parallel to the wall if the backfill is greater than 1.5 m (5 ft.), and follow CSA nailing requirements for floor sheathing. It is advisable to block between the floor joists above each sleeper (see Figure 51a).

◆ For a suspended wood floor, align joists with the wall studs and toe-nail to a continuous ledger, double the joists where parallel to the wall, provide ladder-type blocking where backfill is greater than 2 m (6 ft., 6 in.) and follow CSA nailing requirements for floor sheathing (see Figure 51b).

◆ Where basement floor joists are not continuous, avoid lapped joints. Butt joists end-to-end and use galvanized side straps or scabbing for reinforcement.

Protruding nails at 400 mm (16 in.) o.c.

Concrete floor slab

Moisture barrier

19 x 64-mm (1 x 3-in.) screed board

25 mm (1 in.)

FIGURE 50
CONCRETE-SLAB FLOOR

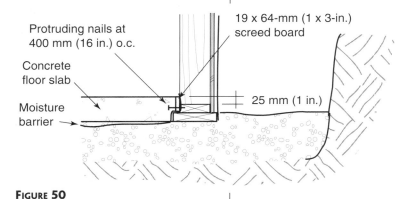

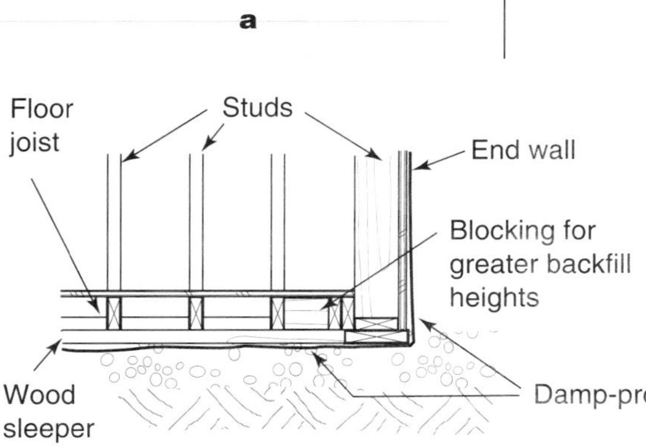

a

Floor joist

Studs

End wall

Blocking for greater backfill heights

Wood sleeper

Damp-proofing

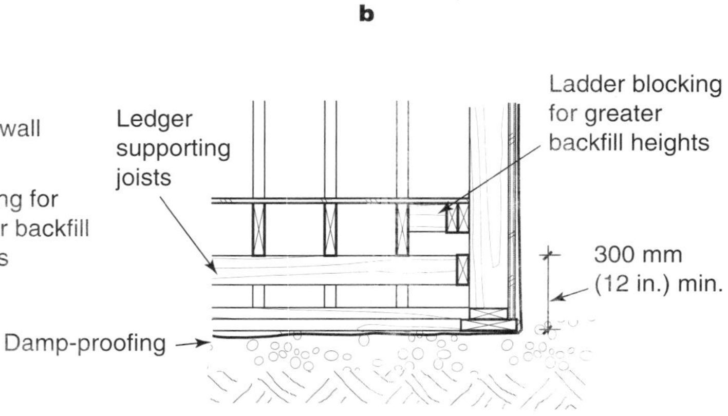

b

Ledger supporting joists

Ladder blocking for greater backfill heights

300 mm (12 in.) min.

FIGURE 51
PRESERVED-WOOD BASEMENT FLOOR SYSTEMS

PROBLEM
DEFLECTION FROM SOIL PRESSURE

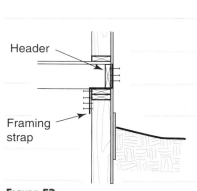

Header

Framing strap

FIGURE 52
FRAMING STRAPS

CAUSE

Lack of lateral support at the top of the wall

SOLUTIONS

◆ Align main floor joists with wall studs where possible.

◆ If floor joists and wall studs have different spacings, use framing straps to connect the inner face of the studs to the outer face of the header or rim joist (see Figure 52).

◆ With deeper backfill, use framing straps or joist hangers. This will greatly decrease the possibility of wall–floor separation. In some cases, a 38 x 89-mm (2 x 4-in.) reinforcement can be spiked to the underside of the floor joists as a remedial measure when backfill is deeper than originally planned. Check with your local building officials.

◆ Where joists run parallel to the wall, provide full depth blocking in line with the wall studs in the first joist space. With greater backfill heights, add a 38 x 89-mm (2 x 4-in.) joist reinforcement to provide increased nailing surface for the floor sheathing (see Figure 53), or install blocking in the second joist space.

◆ Special conditions, such as very narrow buildings, extra long walls, or sloping sites, may require the use of partitions as shear walls for added lateral support to prevent racking, and they will require an engineered design.

◆ If a single top plate is used, locate joists directly over studs and provide metal straps over plate joints for reinforcement.

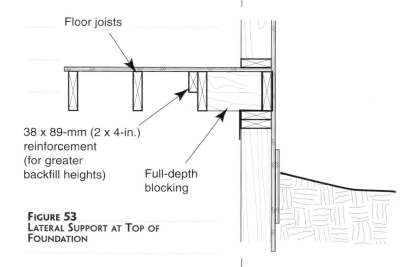

Floor joists

38 x 89-mm (2 x 4-in.) reinforcement (for greater backfill heights)

Full-depth blocking

FIGURE 53
LATERAL SUPPORT AT TOP OF FOUNDATION

PROBLEM

DEFLECTION FROM SOIL PRESSURE

CAUSE

Lack of lateral support with manufactured floor framing

The use of floor trusses, wood "I" beams, and other manufactured products as an alternative to conventional floor joists is increasing. Such systems require special attention for lateral support at the end walls.

SOLUTIONS

◆ Extend end walls so that the top plate is level with the top of the floor trusses. For greater backfill heights, provide 38 x 89-mm (2 x 4-in.) blocking to help transfer loads from the wall to the top chord of the truss (see Figure 54).

◆ Alternatively, if a stub wall is installed on the end wall, extend the diagonal bracing to the second truss to prevent uplift of the floor (see Figure 55). The bracing should be kept at an angle of less than 30 degrees to prevent uplift.

◆ Seek advice from the manufacturer or an engineer on the use of blocking with glulam and manufactured framing members.

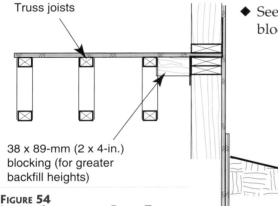

Truss joists

38 x 89-mm (2 x 4-in.) blocking (for greater backfill heights)

FIGURE 54
LATERAL SUPPORT WITH FLOOR TRUSSES

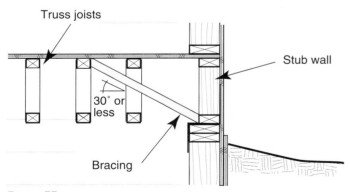

Truss joists

Stub wall

30° or less

Bracing

FIGURE 55
LATERAL SUPPORT WITH FLOOR TRUSSES

PROBLEM
DEFLECTION FROM SOIL PRESSURE

CAUSE

Lack of lateral support at wall and floor openings

Large, unsupported openings can be a major cause of failures.

SOLUTIONS

◆ Use framing anchors at all framing around window openings, and framing straps over lintels, to help transfer soil pressures. Increase the number of studs and sill plates for larger openings (see Figure 56).

◆ Provide additional framing where stairwells are within 1.2 m (4 ft.) of a side wall or 1.8 m (6 ft.) of an end wall.

– Near an end wall, double the trimmer joists, add horizontal members in the joist space above the studs to create a beam, and reinforce the header with cripples (see Figure 57).

– Near a side wall, create a beam over the wall as above, or add a horizontal member across the underside of the double trimmer joists.

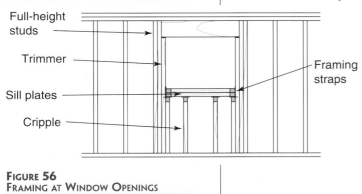

Full-height studs

Trimmer

Sill plates

Cripple

Framing straps

FIGURE 56
FRAMING AT WINDOW OPENINGS

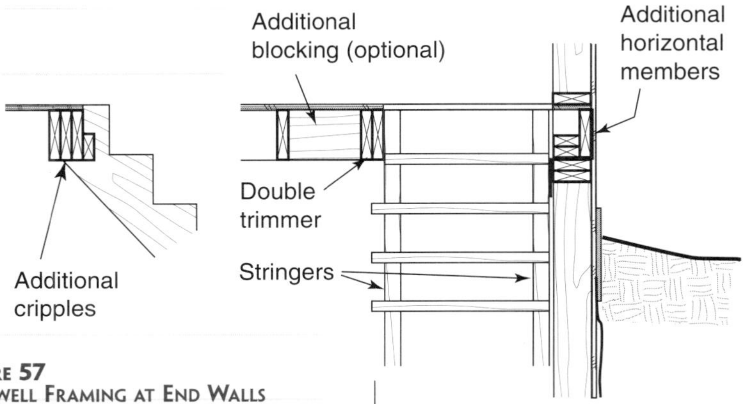

Additional blocking (optional)

Additional horizontal members

Double trimmer

Stringers

Additional cripples

FIGURE 57
STAIRWELL FRAMING AT END WALLS

PROBLEM
DEFLECTION FROM SOIL PRESSURE

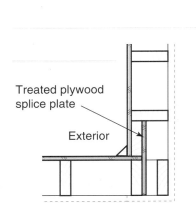

Treated plywood
splice plate

Exterior

FIGURE 58
INSIDE-CORNER DETAILS

CAUSE

Lack of support at interior corners

Soil loads may force joints open where a building configuration has an interior corner.

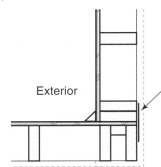

Exterior

Galvanized steel strap
at 300 mm (12 in.) o.c.

SOLUTIONS

◆ Reinforce interior corners with plywood splice plates or with galvanized straps and extra studding (see Figure 58).

◆ Lap the wall plate and footing plate. Lap doubled top plates.

CAUSE

Poor backfilling practices

SOLUTIONS

◆ Do not backfill until both the main floor and the basement floor are in place, or until the walls are adequately braced top and bottom. Backfill evenly with small lifts, starting at the corners. Use granular fill. Have bulldozer operators lift their blades as they approach the wall. Avoid driving heavy equipment close to the walls.

◆ For unexcavated crawl spaces, backfill both sides of the wall (see Figure 59).

◆ If backfill heights on opposite sides of the building differ by more than 600 mm (2 ft.), such as in a walk-out basement, racking of the end walls may occur. Seek engineering advice regarding additional end-wall nailing and structural use of partitions.

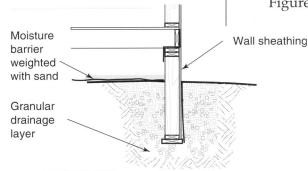

Moisture
barrier
weighted
with sand

Wall sheathing

Granular
drainage
layer

FIGURE 59
UNEXCAVATED CRAWL SPACE

1.3.2 WATER LEAKAGE
PROBLEM
LEAKAGE AND MOISTURE DAMAGE

The preservatives used in PWF materials are meant to inhibit decay, not to make foundations waterproof. To ensure satisfactory performance of the foundation and to protect interior finishes from damage, it is necessary to provide good site drainage and a moisture barrier.

CAUSE

Lack of good site drainage

Correcting a poorly drained foundation can be a difficult and expensive operation. The effort invested in providing good subsurface drainage is well worth it.

SOLUTIONS

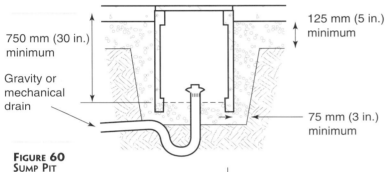

750 mm (30 in.) minimum

125 mm (5 in.) minimum

Gravity or mechanical drain

75 mm (3 in.) minimum

FIGURE 60
SUMP PIT

◆ Provide a continuous drainage pad at least 125 mm (5 in.) deep under the entire foundation area. Extend the drainage layer at least 300 mm (12 in.) beyond the footing. Suitable materials include crushed rock, pea gravel, riverbank gravel, or pit run with few fines. Drainage should be clean and free from silt.

◆ Protect the drainage layer from contamination by native soil, fine sand, and organic matter during the construction process.

◆ Slope the excavation to a central sump pit. Make channels with a shovel to ensure drainage from low spots in the excavation.

◆ Build the sump pit at least 750 mm (30 in.) deep, with an area of at least 0.25 m² (2.8 sq. ft.). Provide mechanical or gravity drainage from the sump to a municipal sewer or drainage ditch. Install the drain pipe so that the invert is at least 150 mm (6 in.) below the bottom of the excavation (see Figure 60).

◆ Geotextiles or "filter fabrics" allow the passage of water, but not of fine particles. Sheets of filter fabric can be laid below and around the granular drainage pad to prevent the drainage layer from becoming clogged.

◆ Use a granular, free-draining, non-frost-susceptible backfill, such as clean sand and gravel, to provide a "porous envelope" around the foundation.

◆ Drain from below trenched crawl-space footings. The most convenient location for a sump pit may be along the perimeter of the foundation at the sewer line.

◆ Drain the granular pad below frost walls, such as those used for attached garages (see Figure 61).

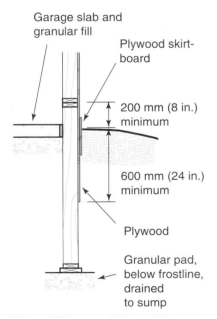

Garage slab and granular fill

Plywood skirtboard

200 mm (8 in.) minimum

600 mm (24 in.) minimum

Plywood

Granular pad, below frostline, drained to sump

FIGURE 61
FROST WALL (GARAGE)

CAUSE

Trapping run-off water with footings

SOLUTIONS

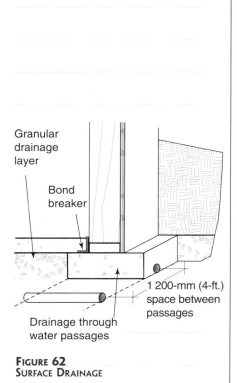

Granular drainage layer

Bond breaker

Drainage through water passages

1 200-mm (4-ft.) space between passages

FIGURE 62
SURFACE DRAINAGE

◆ Avoid "damming" the drainage layer with concrete footings. Install footings above the drainage layer if possible.

◆ If concrete footings are installed on undisturbed subsoil, provide drainage passages of at least 60 mm (2-1/2 in.) in diameter every 1200 mm (4 ft.) to allow water to pass. Protect the passages from becoming plugged during concrete pouring. Ensure that a drainage layer is provided on the exterior of the footing. Make footings no wider than necessary to meet NBC requirements (see Figure 62).

◆ Wood footing plates on a granular pad are preferable to poured concrete footings, since they do not create dams. Some builders find wood footings difficult to level and stabilize. This problem can be overcome if footings are nailed to levelling stakes or if removable stakes are used.

◆ To avoid trapping water with footing plates, do not allow plates to extend more than 50 mm (2 in.) beyond the foundation wall.

PROBLEM
LEAKAGE AND MOISTURE DAMAGE

CAUSE

Incorrect application of moisture barrier (damp-proofing)

Although it is expected that good site drainage will keep PWF structures generally dry, sealed foundation joints and a moisture barrier are required to divert local moisture to the drainage pad. Poor installation of moisture barriers is perhaps the aspect that most weakens preserved-wood foundations.

SOLUTIONS

◆ Leave a 2 to 3-mm (1/8-in.) gap between plywood sheets, and caulk all plywood joints and plywood footing joints to act as a backing for the moisture barrier. The best method is to apply sealant to plywood edges, then mount sheets to press into the bead of sealant. Warm the sealant if the temperature is lower than 5°C (41°F). Do not allow sealants to freeze.

◆ Do not place plywood joints directly below beam pockets and window corners—there could be a certain amount of movement or shrinkage at these points.

◆ The CAN/CSA Standard specifies 0.15-mm (6-mil) CGSB polyethylene as an acceptable moisture barrier. Check with local authorities for acceptance of the following alternatives:

  – Bitumastic coatings, such as those used as damp-proofing on concrete foundations, can be sprayed, brushed, or troweled on.

  – Various resin or plastic coatings, such as thermoplastic rubber (TPR), are also becoming popular and can be sprayed, brushed, or rolled on.

  – Composite membranes similar to those used in commercial waterproofing can be applied directly to the sheathing.

  – Drainage mats or exterior fibrous insulation, although expensive, prevent water from reaching the wall.

◆ Lap polyethylene joints by at least 150 mm (6 in.). Seal only at the top and at each lapped vertical joint. To prevent tearing of the polyethylene,

  – loop the polyethylene behind the skirt board, so that the polyethylene can slide as the backfill settles (see Figure 63a);

  – install polyethylene immediately before backfilling;

  – use heavier or laminated polyethylene;

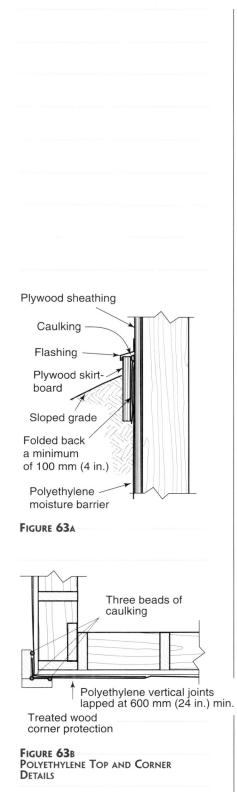

Plywood sheathing

Caulking

Flashing

Plywood skirt-board

Sloped grade

Folded back a minimum of 100 mm (4 in.)

Polyethylene moisture barrier

FIGURE 63A

Three beads of caulking

Polyethylene vertical joints lapped at 600 mm (24 in.) min.

Treated wood corner protection

FIGURE 63B
POLYETHYLENE TOP AND CORNER DETAILS

- protect the polyethylene with fibreboard or exterior insulation; and

- protect lapped polyethylene at exterior corners with corner boards (see Figure 63b).

◆ With coatings, ensure continuity and adequate thickness. This is often difficult to control on site, especially since PWF plywood is unsanded. With sprayed coatings, trowel or spray additional coating into the joints before spraying.

◆ There is considerable variation in bitumastic coatings. Coal-tar-based coatings may last longer than those that are asphalt-based, because of their greater resistance to soil microbes. Solvent-based coatings may be more permanent than emulsion-based. Fibrated coatings have improved durability.

◆ To avoid trapping moisture in the foundation wall with a possible "double vapour barrier,"

- do not seal the polyethylene to the footing, so that trapped water may drain (see Figure 64);

- use a breathable sheet material or coating for a moisture barrier; or

- vent PWF wall cavities by drilling holes through the top plates.

◆ Use types or combinations of damp-proofing methods appropriate to the site and soil conditions. Factors that increase the risk of moisture problems include poor soil drainage, a high water table, and high annual rainfall or snowfall.

◆ For higher risk areas, provide exterior fibrous insulation or a "drainage mat" over the moisture barrier: run-off water will be carried vertically to the base of the footing and will not penetrate to the foundation wall.

◆ Protect the moisture barrier at grade using one of the following methods:

- a 300-mm (12-in.)-wide cover of PWF plywood extending at least 75 mm (3 in.) above grade or, if using cladding susceptible to moisture damage, a wider cover extending at least 200 mm (8 in.) above grade;

- flashing; or

- parging on wire mesh.

◆ Seal all openings where mechanical services penetrate the moisture barrier.

◆ Provide a strip of polyethylene between the footing and bottom plate to prevent moisture from migrating up through capillary action.

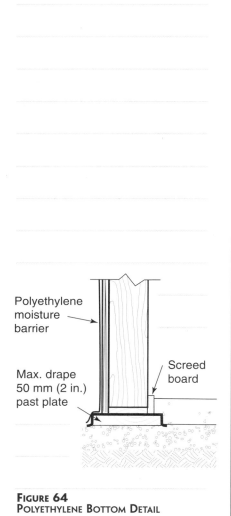

Polyethylene moisture barrier

Screed board

Max. drape 50 mm (2 in.) past plate

FIGURE 64
POLYETHYLENE BOTTOM DETAIL

PROBLEM
LEAKAGE AND MOISTURE DAMAGE

CAUSE

Improper installation of damp-proofing and soil-gas control below floor

SOLUTIONS

Concern has been growing in recent years over the possible effect of soil gases, such as radon, on human health. Radon gas results from the natural radioactive decay of radon found in soil, rock, and ground water. It can enter the house through air leakage below grade.

◆ Beneath a concrete floor slab, provide 0.15-mm (6-mil) poly-ethylene or Type S roll roofing, lapped a minimum of 300 mm (12 in.) and sealed at all edges and penetrations.

◆ With a suspended wood floor or wood sleeper floor, provide poly-ethylene as damp-proofing and for soil-gas control. The polyethyl-ene should be lapped a minimum of 300 mm (12 in.) and extended up the foundation walls to be sealed to the wall air barrier (see Figure 65).

◆ To allow drainage for future spills, slope the moisture barrier to the sump pit, and do not seal the joints in the polyethylene. Do not extend polyethylene under the footing plate, since this may trap water against the underside of the footing.

◆ Seal all penetrations through the floor with a flexible sealant.

◆ Provide a strip of polyethylene between the footing and bottom plate to prevent moisture from migrating up through capillary action.

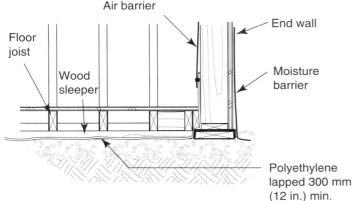

Air barrier

End wall

Floor joist

Wood sleeper

Moisture barrier

Polyethylene lapped 300 mm (12 in.) min.

FIGURE 65
SOIL-GAS CONTROL

PROBLEM
LEAKAGE AND MOISTURE DAMAGE

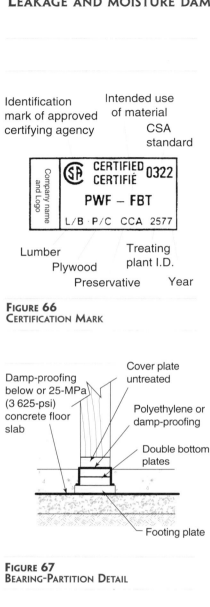

Identification mark of approved certifying agency

Intended use of material
CSA standard

Company name and Logo

CERTIFIED 0322
CERTIFIÉ

PWF – FBT

L/B · P/C CCA 2577

Lumber
Plywood

Treating plant I.D.

Preservative   Year

FIGURE 66
CERTIFICATION MARK

Damp-proofing below or 25-MPa (3 625-psi) concrete floor slab

Cover plate untreated

Polyethylene or damp-proofing

Double bottom plates

Footing plate

FIGURE 67
BEARING-PARTITION DETAIL

CAUSE

Unsuitable materials

SOLUTIONS

◆ Use certified materials only. Look for "PWF" on the certification stamp. Material must be produced by a plant that has a quality control program that meets the requirements of CSA 0322. This was formerly administered by CSA, but is now done by a number of certifying agencies (see Figure 66).

◆ Don't confuse PWF materials with other treated materials used for deck and exterior construction.

 – PWF materials are treated to higher retentions than normal pressure-treated woods, and can be identified by incision marks.

 – Creosote and pentachlorophenol may leach out with time and are not approved for use in a preserved-wood foundation.

 – PWF preservatives are bonded to the wood cell walls by a chemical reaction and do not leach out.

◆ Untreated materials can only be used in the following locations:

 – wall sheathing, lintels, headers and top plates, if they are 200 mm (8 in.) above finish grade;

 – floor framing support beams and floor sheathing, if they are 300 mm (12 in.) above the granular drainage layer (note that the NBC requires all crawl spaces to be ventilated); and

 – interior columns and partitions, if they are above a suspended floor or separated from a concrete slab by damp-proofing; a load-bearing interior partition may require a triple bottom plate (see Figure 67).

◆ Use only corrosion-resistant fasteners:

 – hot-dipped galvanized nails or stainless steel;

 – stainless-steel staples (their diameter is smaller than nails); and

 – 0.9-mm (20-gauge) hot-dipped galvanized framing anchors and straps.

 Do not use electro-galvanized or aluminum fasteners.

◆ Use sealants that are watertight and do not dry out, such as butyl-polyisobutylene polymer or elastomeric. Polysulphides may not adhere well to PWF material without a primer.

◆ Ensure that sealants are compatible with the type of moisture barrier being used. For example, adhesives with a petroleum-based solvent may attack polyethylene.

Cause

Cutting of materials

Preservative penetrates only the outer shells of PWF framing members; the members are therefore susceptible to decay if opened up.

Solutions

◆ Avoid cutting, notching, and drilling materials, if possible.

◆ Order the specific lengths required.

◆ Let footing plates extend beyond walls rather than cut them.

◆ Do not drill openings in the bottom plate for anchor bolts, since this will open up the interior of the wood. Soil pressure and the interior floor should be sufficient to hold the plate in place. If mechanical fastening is necessary, use power nailing with high-carbon concrete nails.

◆ Do not run plumbing or ductwork in exterior PWF walls.

◆ Do not drill holes in PWF walls for electrical wiring. Where outlets are required, run wiring vertically in stud spaces and drill through the top plate, instead of drilling through wall studs (see Figure 68).

◆ Treat all cut surfaces with a preservative designed specifically for field application, such as copper napthenate. Repeat the application until fluid is no longer absorbed.

◆ Install framing members with cut end up.

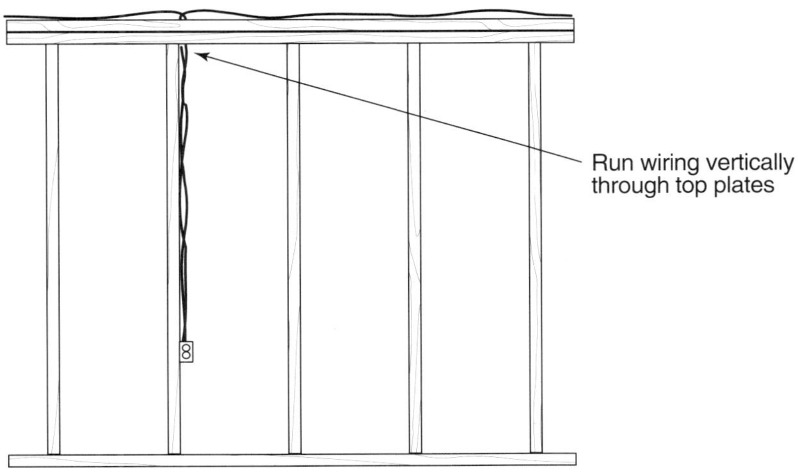

Run wiring vertically through top plates

Figure 68
Electrical Wiring

Section 1.4 Additional Reading

SOURCE	PUBLICATION
Canadian Home Builders' Association 150 Laurier Ave. West, Suite 500 Ottawa ON K1P 5J4 613 230-3060	*CHBA Builders' Manual*, 1994
Canadian Standards Association 178 Rexdale Boulevard Toronto ON M9W 1R3 905 747-2287	*Construction of Preserved Wood Foundations*, 1992 CAN/CSA-S406-92 *Concrete Construction for Housing and Small Buildings* CAN3-A438-M
Canadian Wood Council 1400 Blair Place, Suite 210 Ottawa ON K1J 9B8 613 747-5544	*Permanent Wood Foundations 1992*
National Research Council of Canada Institute for Research in Construction Publications Section Ottawa ON K1A 0R6 In Ottawa: 613 993-2463 Other locations: 1 800 672-7990	*Principles of Foundation Design* CBD 80 *Selecting the Foundation* CBD 81 *Adfreezing and Frost Heaving of Foundations* CBD 128 *Foundation Movements* CBD 148 *Drainage around Buildings* CBD 156 *Frost Action and Foundations* CBD 182 *Foundations on Swelling or Shifting Soils* CBD 184
National Association of Home Builders Home Builders' Book Store 1201 15th Street N.W. Washington, D.C. 20005 202 223-2665	*Frost-Protected Shallow Foundations*, 1994
Ontario New Home Warranty Program 5160 Yonge Street, 6th Floor North York ON M2N 6L9 416 229-9200	*Soils Manual For Home Builders*, 1996 *Better Basements: Construction Practice Booklet*, 1995

2.1.1 NOISE PROBLEMS
PROBLEM
FLOOR SQUEAKS

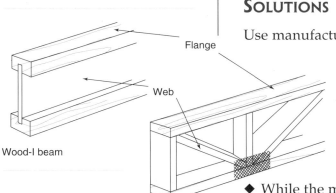

Wood-I beam

Floor truss

FIGURE 1
MANUFACTURED ENGINEERED MEMBERS

Flange

Web

CAUSE

Lumber shrinkage

As dimensional lumber dries, it shrinks. When shrinkage occurs, the fasteners loosen and effectively lose their grip on the subfloor. As the subfloor flexes under loads, it rubs against the fasteners, floor joists, or against other subfloor panels, producing a squeak or creak.

SOLUTIONS

Use manufactured engineered members.

◆ Manufactured engineered members are constructed of dry, dimensionally stable materials. The flanges are constructed from dimensional lumber, and the webs are made of dimensional lumber, wood panels, or metal. Manufactured engineered members remain dimensionally stable as moisture content remains relatively constant (see Figure 1).

◆ While the manufactured engineered members themselves do not shrink, you must take care where they are connected to other materials. Properly fasten the subfloor to structural members, and use adhesive to fasten the subfloor to manufactured structural members. This will reduce squeaks and improve floor performance.

◆ See Chapter 6 for more information on noise control.

Use dry lumber and allow time for shrinkage.

Using dry lumber, and allowing time for shrinkage to take place will reduce or even eliminate the amount of shrinkage that will occur.

The NBC requires that the moisture content of lumber be not more than 19 percent when it is installed. S-DRY lumber must be at 19 percent moisture content or less when it is manufactured. You will minimize the amount of shrinkage by specifying this material and protecting it on site.

◆ Using kiln-dried lumber will not necessarily eliminate shrinkage. Kiln-dried lumber can continue to shrink after leaving the kiln until the cells reach atmospheric moisture content (approximately 8 percent at 50 percent relative humidity [RH]). Even though kiln-dried lumber continues to shrink and can cause minor problems after the wood is installed in the building, these problems will be less severe than if green lumber (S-GRN) is used.

◆ Once installed, wood can dry to an even lower moisture content. Within the first year, wood usually dries to about 10 percent moisture content. By allowing the floor joists to dry for as long as

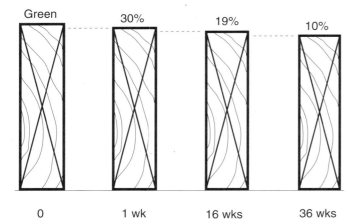

Green	30%	19%	10%
0	1 wk	16 wks	36 wks

FIGURE 2
SHRINKAGE VS. MOISTURE CONTENT FOR KILN-DRIED LUMBER

possible in the house before you perform the final fastening, you can reduce the amount of squeaking that occurs. You must check fasteners and, where necessary, install additional fasteners before you install the final flooring (see Figure 2).

Securely fasten subfloor to joists.

By using other fasteners (staples and screws) and adhesives to fasten the subfloor to the joists, you can help overcome the effects of shrinkage.

Use glue in addition to nails or staples to enhance the fastening of the subfloor to the joists. This technique relies initially on the holding strength of the nails or staples to secure the subfloor to the joists while the glue sets up. Glue may provide as much or more holding capacity as nails or staples, depending upon the type of glue and the conditions under which it is applied.

◆ One benefit of using glue is that it is not affected by shrinkage in the same way that mechanical fasteners are affected. Glue is used only on the top of the joist and therefore shrinkage across the depth of the joist will not affect the connection. Follow the manufacturer's installation instructions.

◆ The use of screws instead of nails is becoming more common. Some builders are using glue plus screws in an attempt to eliminate squeaks. Fasteners that are driven 50 mm (2 in.) into the joists have good holding strength until the joist shrinks. As the wood shrinks, the amount of fastener that remains embedded in the joists may be reduced by 3 mm (1/8 in.) or more. In effect, the fastener releases its hold on the subfloor. This "popping" of the fastener allows the subfloor to move and results in a squeak (see Figure 3).

Joist before shrinkage

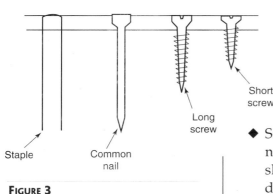

After drying of joist

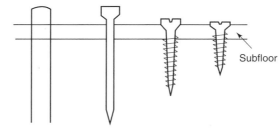

Subfloor

Short screw

Long screw

Staple

Common nail

FIGURE 3
EFFECT OF WOOD SHRINKAGE ON FASTENERS

◆ Since screws have 25 to 75 percent more holding strength than nails of a similar diameter, you may use shorter screws. The shorter the fastener, the less susceptible it will be to "popping" due to shrinkage of the joists.

◆ Ensure fasteners are embedded in joists. Nails or screws which miss the joists can rub against the wood when it is under loading.

PROBLEM
FLOOR SQUEAKS

CAUSE

Subfloor movement

Most subfloor movement takes place at the edges of panels, where they are the weakest. When the edge of a panel between floor joists carries a concentrated load, such as a person walking across the floor, the edge of the panel deflects. This deflection may be small, but if the neighbouring panel is not loaded, squeaking may occur as the two panel edges rub against each other.

SOLUTIONS

Provide backing or blocking at panel edges.

◆ Check all subfloor panels for damage before installation.

◆ The simplest way to eliminate movement for square-edged panels is to install blocking between the joists at all panel edges. Edge blocking is only required by the NBC in certain situations. However, in higher traffic areas, it may be worth the time and effort to block all panel edges to eliminate movement between subfloor panels. Blocking must be installed properly to prevent it from becoming a source of squeaks rather than a means of eliminating them (see Figure 4).

◆ While the NBC requires that blocking not be less than 38 x 38 mm (2 x 2 in.), 38 x 89-mm (2 x 4-in.) material provides more structural support for the edges of the subfloor panels. In locations of ducting and other obstacles, the blocking can be installed on the flat. In all cases, the top of the blocking must be flush with the top of the floor joists.

Space panels.

◆ Leaving a gap between square-edged panels ensures that the deflection between joists due to loading will not result in edges rubbing on each other. The gap also allows for panel expansion, should site conditions cause the panel to swell. The NBC does not specify spacing between subfloor panels, but most subfloor panel manufacturers recommend a spacing of about 3 mm (1/8 in.)

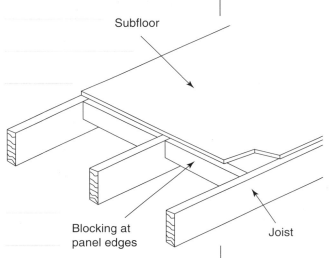

Subfloor

Blocking at
panel edges

Joist

FIGURE 4
PANEL-EDGE SUPPORT

Use tongue-and-groove panels.

Interlocking the panel edges by using tongue-and-groove subflooring provides a supporting effect similar to that of blocking the panel edges. The loads on one panel are effectively transferred to the adjoining interlocking panel. Movement between panels is virtually eliminated.

◆ Ensure that the tongue portion of the panel is not damaged, as this can actually create squeaks. Tongue damage can occur if the panels are forced together.

Fasten edges of panels.

◆ Properly fastening the panel edges can reduce the amount of subfloor movement, especially when the fastening is done in combination with installing tongue-and-groove panels or placing blocking at panel edges. The NBC requires that fasteners be installed at 150 mm (6 in.) o.c. along edges and at 300 mm (12 in.) o.c. along intermediate supports. The manufacturers of subfloor panels recommend the same spacing for panel edges but some recommend 250 mm (10 in.) o.c. along intermediate supports (see Figure 5). The types of fasteners (nails, screws, staples, glue) were discussed in section 2.1.1.

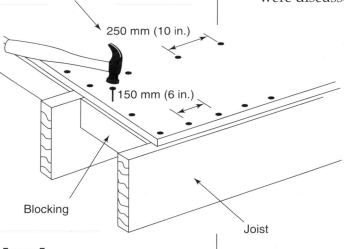

Subfloor

250 mm (10 in.)

150 mm (6 in.)

Blocking

Joist

FIGURE 5
FASTENING OF PANEL EDGES

PROBLEM
FLOOR SQUEAKS

CAUSE

Underlay movement

Underlay panels do not move if they have been installed properly on a solid base. Fasteners that are not fully secured or become loose will allow the underlay panels to move up and down on the shaft of the fastener, resulting in squeaking. If the fasteners are loose, or if an insufficient number of fasteners is installed, the edges of the underlay panels can rub against one another, causing squeaking.

SOLUTIONS

Fasten the underlay adequately.

◆ Fastening the underlay panels is critical to eliminating movement. The NBC requires that staples, annular grooved floor nails, or spiral nails be installed not more than 150 mm (6 in.) o.c. along the edges and not more than 200 mm (8 in.) o.c. both ways at other locations. The underlay manufacturers recommend even closer spacings between 50 mm (2 in.) o.c. and 100 mm (4 in.) o.c. along edges and between 100 mm (4 in.) o.c. and 150 mm (6 in.) o.c. at other locations (see Figure 6).

◆ Some builders use glue along with staples or nails when installing underlay.

Install underlay on a strong, stable base.

◆ Any movement of the underlay can result in squeaking and problems with the finish flooring. If the subfloor is spongy and moves when loaded, the underlay will squeak along panel edges. Follow the NBC or manufacturer recommendations for base requirements.

◆ Joints in underlay panels must be offset more than 200 mm (8 in.) from joints in subfloor panels.

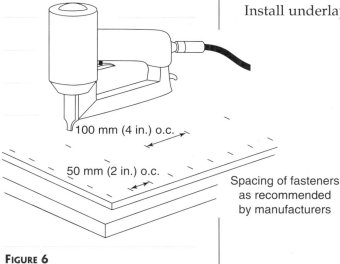

100 mm (4 in.) o.c.

50 mm (2 in.) o.c.

Spacing of fasteners as recommended by manufacturers

FIGURE 6
FASTENING UNDERLAY PANELS TO THE SUBFLOOR

2.1.2 INADEQUATE SUPPORT PROBLEM

WOOD-I JOISTS ARE OVERSTRESSED AROUND PERIMETER

CAUSE

Wood-I joists have limited capacity to transfer roof and floor loads vertically from above.

SOLUTIONS

Ensure properly sized rim joists with full bearings.

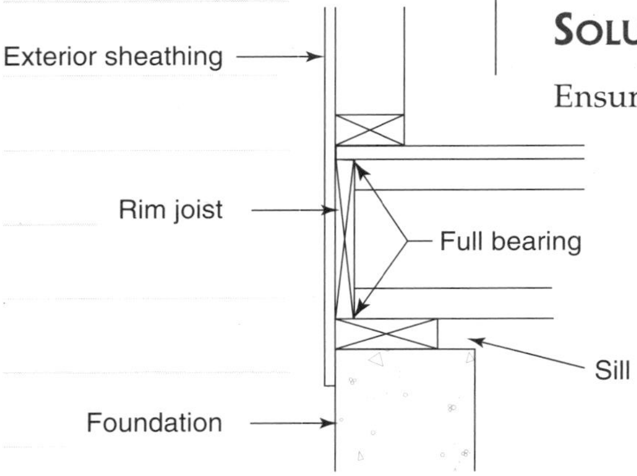

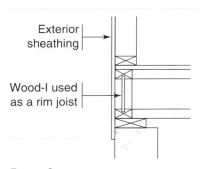

FIGURE 7
ADEQUATE RIM BOARD WITH PROPER BEARING

- ◆ Rim joists can be used to transfer vertical loads from above, through the floor system, and down to the support below. Rim boards have varying requirements, depending on the loading conditions. The manufacturer's design must be followed (see Figure 7).
- ◆ The rim boards used for the main floor of a two-storey house must be thicker than the rim boards used for the second floor of the same two-storey house.
- ◆ Rim boards must be installed so that they have full bearing at the top and at the bottom. If full bearing contact is not achieved, the rim board cannot transfer the required loads.
- ◆ Wood-I floor joists that are subject to excessive loads (because of faulty rim board installation) can twist or crush, resulting in serious structural failure of the floor system.

Install wood-I rim joists or blocking panels.

- ◆ Rim joists or blocking panels can be used instead of rim boards. Rim joists are wood-I joists that run around the perimeter of the floor system to transfer the vertical loads from above. Sawn lumber is not used, as it will shrink and transfer loads to the floor joists. Care must be taken when using wood-I joists as rim joists to ensure that the floor joists have adequate bearing on the wall or sill plate. Check the manufacturer's requirements for minimum bearing lengths (see Figure 8).
- ◆ Blocking panels are short sections of the wood-I floor joist that fit between the floor joists. These short sections transfer the vertical loads through the floor system in the same manner as rim joists.
- ◆ When rim joists or blocking panels are used, closure panels must be installed around the perimeter. These are simply strips of wall sheathing that enclose the floor system and provide support for the exterior finish.
- ◆ Ensure wood-I floor joists have sufficient room for end bearing. If blocking panels are used, floor joists can extend to the outside of the foundation or bearing wall.

FIGURE 8
WOOD-I JOIST/BLOCKING PANEL USED FOR PERIMETER SUPPORT

Install squash blocks.

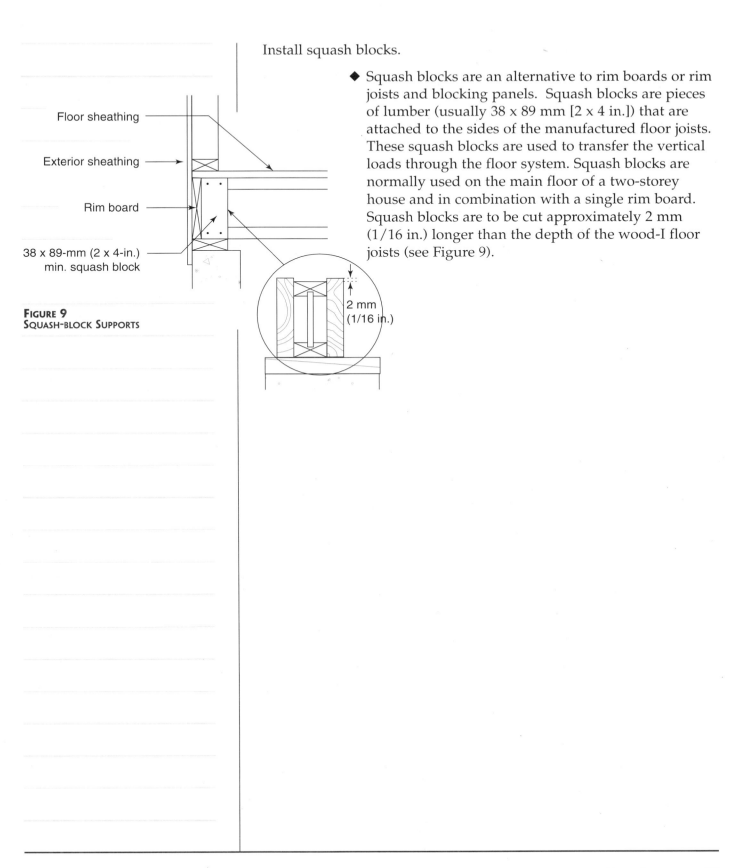

Floor sheathing

Exterior sheathing

Rim board

38 x 89-mm (2 x 4-in.)
min. squash block

2 mm
(1/16 in.)

FIGURE 9
SQUASH-BLOCK SUPPORTS

◆ Squash blocks are an alternative to rim boards or rim joists and blocking panels. Squash blocks are pieces of lumber (usually 38 x 89 mm [2 x 4 in.]) that are attached to the sides of the manufactured floor joists. These squash blocks are used to transfer the vertical loads through the floor system. Squash blocks are normally used on the main floor of a two-storey house and in combination with a single rim board. Squash blocks are to be cut approximately 2 mm (1/16 in.) longer than the depth of the wood-I floor joists (see Figure 9).

PROBLEM
WOOD-I JOISTS ARE OVERSTRESSED AT POINT LOADS

CAUSE

Wood-I joists are not designed to carry large concentrated loads.

The engineered system is based on the transfer of concentrated loads through the floor system on extra blocking. Wood-I joists can be made more economically when they do not have to be designed to carry concentrated loads.

SOLUTIONS

Install solid blocking to transfer the loads through the floor system.

◆ Install solid blocking under all concentrated loads to carry the load to bearing walls, beams, or the foundation. Jack studs supporting lintels, and columns supporting beams, are the most common situations where concentrated loads are found (see Figure 10).

◆ Solid blocking under point loads is most often made from 38 x 89-mm (2 x 4-in.) or 38 x 140-mm (2 x 6-in.) lumber. The blocking must be slightly longer than the depth of the joists so that the loads are transferred through the floor system to the foundation.

◆ Blocking should be installed when the floor is constructed, not added afterwards. When blocking is installed at the correct time, it will take up the loads as they are applied. It is impossible for blocking added after the subfloor is in place to be of the required length.

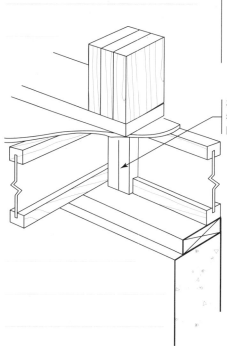

38 x 89-mm (2 x 4-in.) squash blocks to support point load from above

FIGURE 10
BLOCKING CARRYING CONCENTRATED LOADS

PROBLEM
SUPPORT BEAM SAGS

CAUSE

Inadequate beam support

SOLUTIONS

Ensure adequate bearing area for beams. Ensure beams bear evenly on the support.

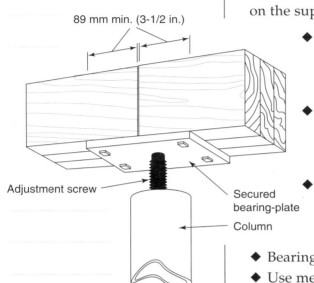

89 mm min. (3-1/2 in.)

Adjustment screw

Secured bearing-plate

Column

FIGURE 11
PROPER BEARING ON BEAM SUPPORTS

◆ At least 89 mm (3-1/2 in.) of the beam must bear evenly on the support. Where individual plys of built-up beams butt over a centre post, each ply must have at least 89 mm (3-1/2 in.) of bearing (see Figure 11).

◆ Make sure that columns are centred on their footings. When columns are not placed in the centre of the footings, the offset loading could cause the column footing to move, thereby causing movement in the column and the beam.

◆ Make sure that the top bearing plates for steel columns are as wide as the beam they support. They must be wide enough to give stability to the connection and to prevent the beam from being crushed by the bearing plate.

◆ Bearing plates must be secured to the beam.

◆ Use metal shims to support beam ends in beam pockets where required.

CAUSE

Beam ends rotting

SOLUTIONS

Protect beam ends that bear on exterior foundation walls at, or below, grade. Beams set into concrete or exposed to high moisture conditions are subject to decay.

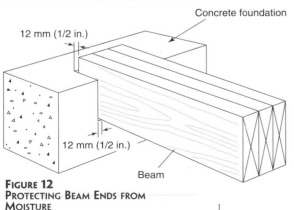

Concrete foundation

12 mm (1/2 in.)

12 mm (1/2 in.)

Beam

FIGURE 12
PROTECTING BEAM ENDS FROM MOISTURE

◆ Protect beam ends that bear on exterior foundation walls at, or below, grade from moisture-induced rotting. Use pressure-treated lumber or provide a 12-mm (1/2-in.) air space all the way around the beam end. The space permits air circulation and moisture evaporation (see Figure 12).

◆ You may protect the ends of beams supported on concrete by wrapping them in polyethylene. This would protect the wood from being exposed to the moisture in the concrete, and it would also allow for the installation of a good, tight air barrier around the end of the beam. This technique works best when the beam is installed in a beam pocket rather than when the beam is cast into the concrete wall.

Section 2.2 Deflection and Vibration
INTRODUCTION

Many people remember hearing dishes rattling whenever someone walked by the china cabinet in their childhood home. Deflection and floor vibration annoy home-owners, and they are usually not identified until after people move into their homes. Bounce is another common complaint about floors. Cracked ceilings, ridges in floors, uneven floors, and obvious movement reveal excessive floor deflection.

When possible, builders should check with home-owners about special loading conditions in their homes or specific furnishings that may be susceptible to vibrations or deflections. Special designs can then be drawn up and precautions taken to accommodate the occupants' requirements.

Properly positioning bearing walls, installing extra blocking, reducing joist spans, or even changing the direction of floor joists can be inexpensive and may help to achieve customer satisfaction. Oversized joists or specialized products such as stress-rated lumber and manufactured floor trusses can also satisfy home-owners' requirements.

Floor vibration is addressed in the NBC span tables. However, it may be necessary to go beyond the requirements of the NBC to achieve the vibration-free floors that some home-owners expect.

2.2.1 VIBRATION AND MOVEMENT PROBLEM

FLOOR VIBRATION

CAUSE

Excessive spans

Vibration-sensitive areas, such as kitchens and dining rooms, may require special attention beyond the spans specified by the NBC for floor joists. Even though the 1995 NBC uses vibration as a criterion for determining allowable spans, there may be instances where the allowable vibration is more than home-owners would like.

SOLUTIONS

Decrease joist spans.

◆ Reducing the distance between supports will reduce the span of the structural members and stiffen the floor system. In a typical floor system with a beam at midspan, adding an additional support will result in sizable reductions in floor vibration (see Figure 13).

Increase depth of joists.

◆ Increasing the depth of joists while retaining spacing can dramatically increase the stiffness of the floor. Since the allowable span controlled by vibration is determined by deflection at midspan, deeper joists are significantly better.

◆ If a floor that is typically constructed with 38 x 184-mm (2 x 8-in.) joists is instead constructed using 38 x 235-mm (2 x 10-in.) joists, the increase in the maximum span controlled by vibration increases by approximately 18 per cent. Switching from 38 x 286-mm (2 x 12-in.) construction to 38 x 235-mm (2 x 10-in.) construction results in an increase in the maximum span controlled by vibration by about 14 percent (see Figure 14).

◆ If you plan to use deeper joists, think about the amount of shrinkage that will take place. Joist shrinkage can cause other problems, such as drywall cracking. The deeper the members are, the greater the shrinkage that may occur.

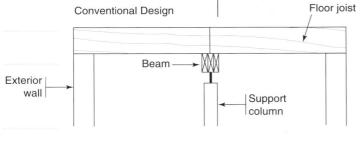

Conventional Design

Floor joist

Beam →

Exterior wall →

Support column

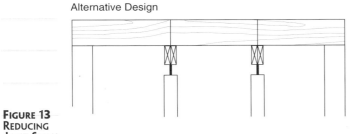

Alternative Design

FIGURE 13
REDUCING
JOIST SPANS

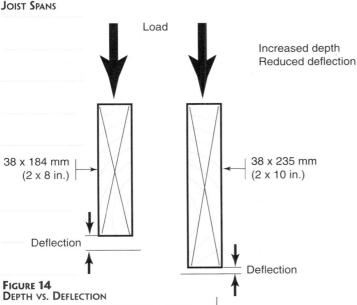

Load

Increased depth
Reduced deflection

38 x 184 mm
(2 x 8 in.)

38 x 235 mm
(2 x 10 in.)

Deflection

Deflection

FIGURE 14
DEPTH VS. DEFLECTION

Decrease joist spacing.

◆ Another option to stiffen the floor system is to decrease the spacing between the joists. This strategy is not as effective as increasing the depth of the joists, but it will have considerable impact.

◆ When comparing 38 x 235-mm (2 x 10-in.) joists at 400 mm (16 in.) o.c. to the same 38 x 235-mm (2 x 10-in.) joists at 300 mm (12 in.) o.c., the maximum allowable span controlled by vibration increases by about 5 percent. This option has very little impact on the design of the house.

◆ Another advantage of closer joist spacing is the reduction in the amount of flexing of the subfloor. This makes the floor feel stronger and helps prevent subfloor ridging.

Use stiffer species of wood.

◆ Choosing a species of wood that is stronger will decrease the vibration. Selecting a species such as Douglas fir rather than spruce can increase the allowable vibration-controlled span by about 5 percent.

◆ As machine stress-rated (MSR) lumber becomes easier to obtain, it may be specified for floor systems. Using MSR joists instead of S-P-F will result in an increase of about 9 percent in the allowable vibration-controlled span.

Glue subfloor and/or use thicker panels.

◆ The floor joists and the subfloor act as a system. Changing the thickness of the subfloor and using a better fastening system can stiffen the floor.

◆ An excellent technique that can be used to stiffen the floor is to glue the subfloor as well as nailing or stapling it. This increases the bonding of the subfloor to the joists and will result in an increase of about 11 percent in the allowable vibration-controlled span.

◆ For maximum benefit when gluing the subfloor to the joists, ensure that both the joists and the subflooring are clean and free of concrete, dirt, moisture, or frost.

◆ Choosing a thicker subfloor will also stiffen the floor. Increasing the subfloor thickness from 15.5 mm (5/8 in.) to 19 mm (3/4 in.) will result in an increase of about 5.5 percent in the allowable vibration controlled span.

PROBLEM

Floor vibration

Cause

Inadequate bridging or blocking

The overall floor system stiffens when blocking and bridging transfer loads from one structural member to another. In order for blocking and bridging to work well, they must be installed properly. Blocking and bridging that are too long or too short or not fastened adequately will not perform.

Solutions

Increase bridging or blocking beyond NBC requirements.

◆ The NBC requires strapping or bridging/blocking once certain spans are exceeded. This improves the load-sharing between structural members, thereby strengthening the floor system.

◆ In vibration-sensitive areas, it may be wise to install two rows of bridging or blocking within the span instead of the one that may be required by the NBC. When more than one row of bridging or blocking is placed near the centre of the floor span, greater stiffness results (see Figure 15).

Use strapping in addition to bridging and blocking.

◆ Strapping on the underside of joists will provide some lateral stability to the joists and prevent twisting, but it does not have much effect on load-sharing. Bridging or blocking is more effective in transferring loads from one structural member to another and thus stiffens the floor, decreasing vibration. The combination of strapping plus either bridging or blocking is even more effective (see Figure 16).

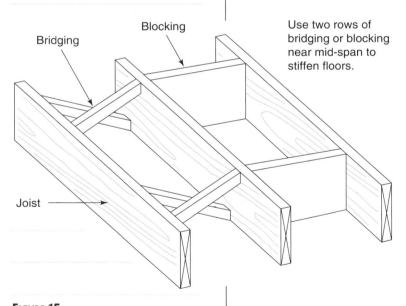

Bridging

Blocking

Use two rows of bridging or blocking near mid-span to stiffen floors.

Joist

Figure 15
Extra Bridging and Blocking to Reduce Vibration

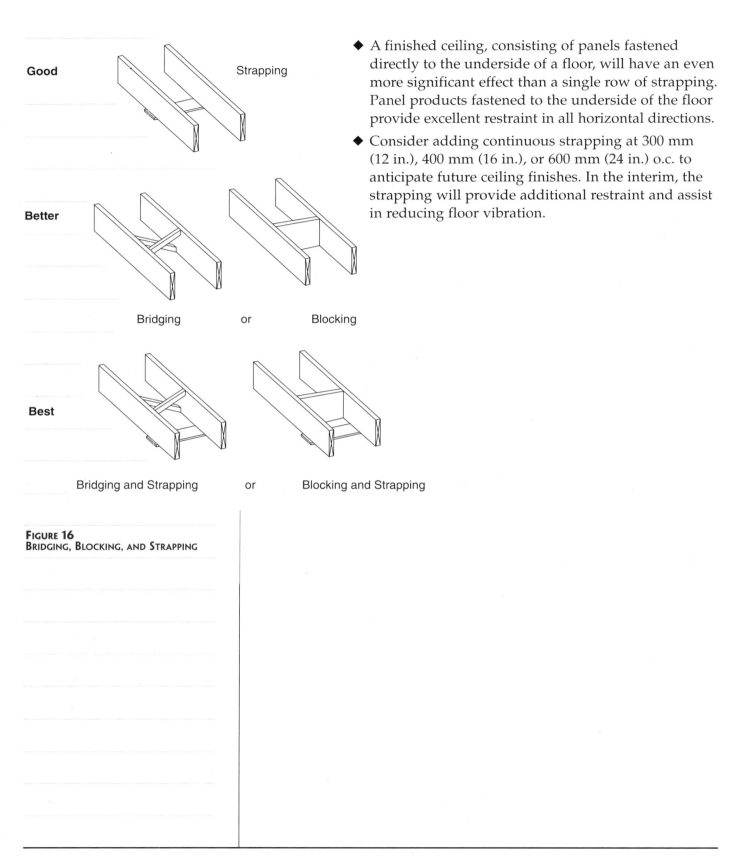

Good
Strapping

Better
Bridging   or   Blocking

Best
Bridging and Strapping   or   Blocking and Strapping

FIGURE 16
BRIDGING, BLOCKING, AND STRAPPING

◆ A finished ceiling, consisting of panels fastened directly to the underside of a floor, will have an even more significant effect than a single row of strapping. Panel products fastened to the underside of the floor provide excellent restraint in all horizontal directions.

◆ Consider adding continuous strapping at 300 mm (12 in.), 400 mm (16 in.), or 600 mm (24 in.) o.c. to anticipate future ceiling finishes. In the interim, the strapping will provide additional restraint and assist in reducing floor vibration.

2.2.2 STRUCTURAL DESIGN PROBLEM

FLOOR VIBRATION

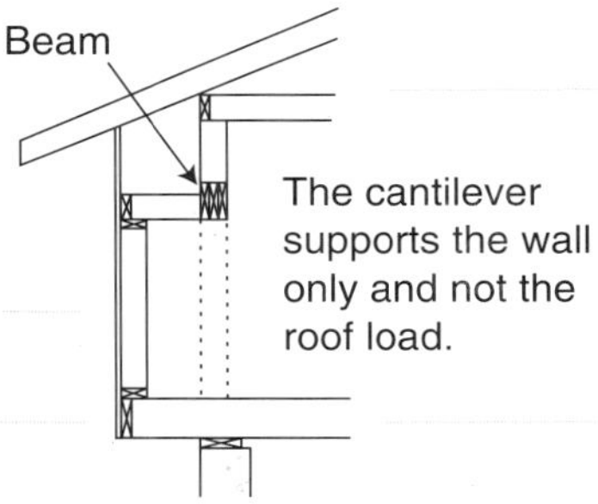

CAUSE

Inappropriate use of cantilevers

Cantilevers can present problems for dining areas, kitchens, built-out china cabinets, and decks or landings. When a load is placed either on the main part of the floor or on the cantilever, the end of the cantilever will experience movement and vibration. Longer cantilevers result in weaker floor systems, which will experience more vibration.

SOLUTIONS

Limit the extension of cantilevers.

◆ The NBC limits the length of cantilevers when they are used to support roof loads. Cantilevers cannot support floor loads from other storeys unless designed professionally.

◆ When joists are cantilevered to accommodate bay windows, recessed china cabinets, extended dinettes, etc., there is a greater possibility that increased vibration will be evident in both the cantilevered section and the main section of the floor. When cantilevers are used, the length must not exceed the NBC maximum.

Limit the load on cantilevers.

◆ In rooms that are enlarged by cantilevering the floor joists, designers should consider using beams to carry roof loads across the openings. Loads are then transferred directly to the foundation with no impact on the floor system (see Figure 17).

◆ If cantilevers are going to be used, it is wise to use them in areas where loading and traffic will be light. Reducing loads on cantilevered joists will minimize the impact on the floor system, and the potential for vibration will be reduced.

Beam

The cantilever supports the wall only and not the roof load.

FIGURE 17
REDUCING LOADS ON CANTILEVERS

PROBLEM
CANTILEVER DEFORMATION

CAUSE

Excessive cantilever spans and/or tail joists

When cantilevers carry both roof loading and live floor loads, movement and deformation can occur both at the cantilever and within the floor system at the opposite end of the cantilever. The length of the cantilever and the length of the tail joists (the inward extension), can affect how significant the deformation will be.

SOLUTIONS

Reduce cantilever span.

◆ As with all structural components in a wood-frame house, joist sizes must be determined using the NBC. Floor joists that support roof loads must not be cantilevered beyond a distance greater than 400 mm (16 in.) for 38 x 184-mm (2 x 8-in.) joists; or beyond 600 mm (24 in.) for 38 x 235-mm (2 x 10-in.) joists (see Figure 18).

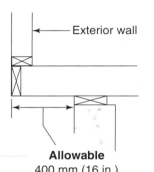

Allowable
400 mm (16 in.)
for 38 x 184-mm (2 x 8-in.) joist

600 mm (24 in.)
for 38 x 235-mm (2 x 10-in.) joist

FIGURE 18
REDUCING CANTILEVER LENGTHS

To Reduce Vibration
Recommended cantilever length
equal to depth of joist

Exterior wall

Extend tail joist length.

◆ When cantilevers are at right angles to the main floor joists, the tail joists (inward extensions) must be extended back into the floor framing by a length at least equal to six times the length of the cantilever. This will prevent an upward movement at the end of the tail joists, especially in high loading situations (see Figure 19).

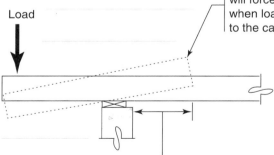

Load

Inadequate inward extension will force the floor to lift when loads are applied to the cantilever

Inadequate inward extension (tail joist)
Minimum extension = 6 times cantilever length

FIGURE 19
CANTILEVER FRAMING

PROBLEM
OVERLOADING OF WOOD-I JOISTS AT CANTILEVERS

CAUSE

Wood-I joists have limited capacity over bearing walls.

When wood-I joists are cantilevered and carry roof loads, there is considerable stress over the bearing wall or beam. The wood-panel webs can become overstressed and fail under severe loading. The high concentrated loads at the bearing support are more than the wood-I joists can handle.

SOLUTIONS

Add web stiffeners.

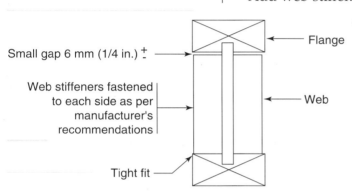

Small gap 6 mm (1/4 in.) ±

Flange

Web stiffeners fastened to each side as per manufacturer's recommendations

Web

Tight fit

FIGURE 20
WEB STIFFENERS

◆ For some loading situations (refer to the manufacturer's recommendations), cantilevered wood-I joists need web stiffeners installed over the support wall. This strengthens the joists at the location where stresses are the highest. Web stiffeners are pieces of blocking (usually plywood or sawn lumber) that are attached to each side of the web between the top and bottom flanges. A 6-mm (1/4-in.) gap is left between the blocking and the top flange (see Figure 20).

◆ Fasten the web stiffeners securely to the web to ensure that the stiffeners and the web act as one unit. This effectively increases the capacity of the web and thus of the structural member over the support, allowing it to carry high loads.

◆ The type and length of fasteners that are required will vary from one manufacturer to another. Always check the manufacturer's requirements, as the fasteners are critical in getting the web stiffeners and the web to act as one unit.

Add reinforcement.

◆ When supporting roof loads, it may be necessary to install reinforcement to the sides of the wood-I joists as per the design professional's requirements. Reinforcement is normally made from sheathing cut to the full depth of the joist and fastened to both the top and bottom flanges. This reinforcement is generally three times the length of the cantilever and extends from the outside of the cantilever into the house. It may be required on one or both sides of the joist.

◆ Another option for reinforcement is to add another section of wood-I joist to the side of the cantilevered joists. The length of the added section is usually three times the length of the cantilever. A filler block is installed between the two webs, and the two sections are fastened securely through the webs and filler block (see Figure 21).

◆ Reinforcement sheathing or joists must be installed when the floor is being framed so that loads imposed by walls, upper floors, and roofs can be handled properly. Once the load has been applied to a joist, adding reinforcement does not necessarily do the job properly. For reinforcement to be useful, it must assume the load at the same time the joist does.

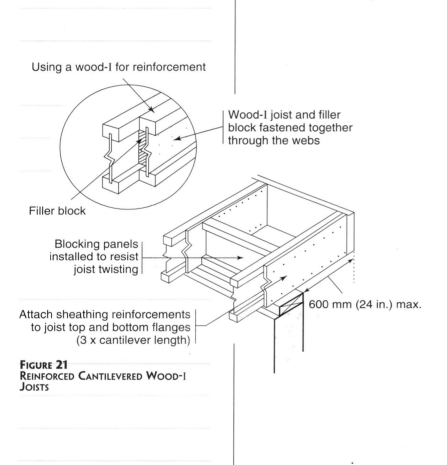

Using a wood-I for reinforcement

Wood-I joist and filler block fastened together through the webs

Filler block

Blocking panels installed to resist joist twisting

Attach sheathing reinforcements to joist top and bottom flanges (3 x cantilever length)

600 mm (24 in.) max.

FIGURE 21
REINFORCED CANTILEVERED WOOD-I JOISTS

PROBLEM
INADEQUATE JOIST SUPPORT

CAUSE

Improper joist bearing

When the bearing surface is too small or the connectors and fastenings are too weak, the joists can move, resulting in sagging of the floor.

SOLUTIONS

Use ledger strips.

◆ Floor joists should have a minimum of 38 mm (1-1/2 in.) of bearing at each end. When joists butt into the side of a beam, a ledger strip can be nailed onto the beam to provide the bearing necessary. Ledger strips are typically 38 x 38 mm (2 x 2 in.) and are fastened to the beam with two 82-mm (3-1/4-in.) nails at each joist. Joists that bear on 38 x 38-mm (2 x 2-in.) ledger strips must also be toe-nailed to the beam with four 89-mm (3-1/2-in.) nails. If 38 x 64-mm (2 x 3-in.) ledger strips are used, you need not toe-nail the joist.

Install joist hangers.

◆ Joist hangers are mechanical fasteners that provide the same support as a ledger strip. Joist hangers are fastened to the wood beam as well as to the joist (see Figure 22).

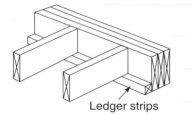

Ledger strips

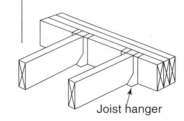

Joist hanger

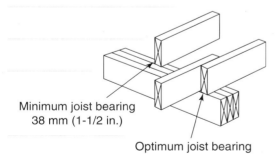

Minimum joist bearing
38 mm (1-1/2 in.)

Optimum joist bearing
full width of beam

FIGURE 22
BEARING SUPPORTS FOR FLOOR JOISTS

PROBLEM
DEFORMATION OF FLOOR JOISTS

CAUSE

Underdesigned floor joists

Floor joists will deflect or deform to some degree, no matter how large or small the load. When joists are installed with the crown or camber up, the deformation from small loads is probably not even noticeable. When the loads are large, the deformations can become excessive to the point where the floor may not be acceptable.

SOLUTIONS

Decrease spans.

◆ The span tables in the NBC should be used to determine the joist size, spacing, and maximum spans permitted. As with beams, the selection of the joist size is a function of the loading, the length of span and the type and grade of lumber.

◆ If unusually large loads are to be applied, decrease the span of the joists. Unusual loading conditions may include the use of concrete toppings, large hot tubs, masonry fireplaces, etc. Professional design is required when such conditions are expected.

Decrease joist spacing or use a stronger species of wood.

◆ Another way to accommodate large loads and reduce deflections is to strengthen the floor system by spacing the joists closer, or using a stronger species of wood.

◆ Spacing joists at 300 mm (12 in.) o.c. rather than 400 mm (16 in.) o.c. will reduce the load carried by each joist by about 25 percent. There should be a corresponding reduction in the amount of deflection that will occur.

◆ Using a stronger species of wood will also reduce the amount of deflection. A property of the wood that affects the amount of deflection is the modulus of elasticity. S-P-F (No. 1) has a modulus of 9 300 while Douglas fir (No. 1) has a modulus of 12 400. The higher the modulus, the stronger the wood, resulting in smaller deflections.

◆ Using a stronger species of wood or decreasing the joist spacing will reduce vibrations as well as deflections.

◆ Stress-rated lumber is much less variable than standard sawn lumber, resulting in stronger members overall. Use stronger lumber to accommodate heavier loads.

PROBLEM
DEFORMATION OF FLOOR JOISTS

CAUSE

Excessive overlapping of joists at beams

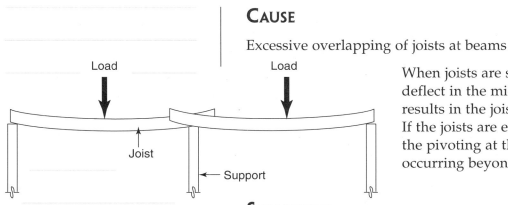

FIGURE 23
EXCESSIVE JOIST OVERLAP AT SUPPORTS

When joists are subjected to loads, they deflect in the middle. This middle deflection results in the joists pivoting at the supports. If the joists are extended over the supports, the pivoting at the end will result in lifting occurring beyond the support (see Figure 23).

SOLUTIONS

Reduce the amount of joist projection beyond the beam.

◆ Since joists will always deflect under load, the effects of the deflection must be minimized. Do not extend joists more than 50 mm (2 in.) beyond the beam. In fact, many builders cut the joists so that they do not overlap, butting them end to end over the support instead. Bottoms of floor joists must be restrained from twisting by toe-nailing to the supports or blocking between the joists (see Figure 24).

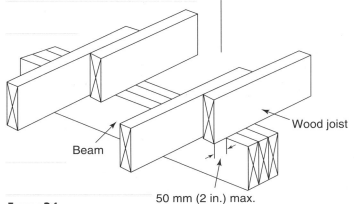

FIGURE 24
PROPER OVERLAP FOR JOISTS

PROBLEM
DEFORMATION OF FLOOR JOISTS

CAUSE

Notching and drilling of joists

When joists are notched or drilled improperly, the effective depth of the joist is decreased. A 38 x 235-mm (2 x 10-in.) joist may perform like a 38 x 184-mm (2 x 8-in.) joist if it is incorrectly notched or drilled. This weakening of the joist can result in excessive deflection or failure.

SOLUTIONS

Keep holes away from the top and bottom edges and from mid-span areas.

◆ Notches, chases, holes, and other penetrations through the joist are often required for plumbing, heating, or electrical services. These can be accommodated if done correctly.

◆ Drill holes no larger than one-quarter the depth of the member. Locate them not less than 50 mm (2 in.) from the edges unless the depth of the member is increased by the size of the hole.

◆ Floor joists can be notched, provided the notch is located on the top of the member within half the joist depth from the edge of the bearing. Do not notch deeper than one-third the joist depth unless you increase the depth of the member by the size of the notch (see Figure 25).

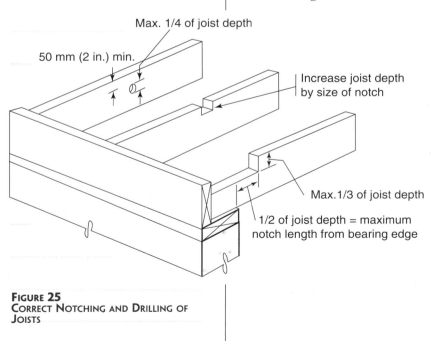

Max. 1/4 of joist depth

50 mm (2 in.) min.

Increase joist depth by size of notch

Max.1/3 of joist depth

1/2 of joist depth = maximum notch length from bearing edge

FIGURE 25
CORRECT NOTCHING AND DRILLING OF JOISTS

Section 2.3 Finish Flooring
INTRODUCTION

Finish flooring is what home-owners see, and problems which develop beneath the flooring are often evident in the finished material. Discoloured resilient flooring is common and the result of different influences. In some cases, non-compatible fillers and adhesives that react with the finish flooring have been used, causing visible problems. Improper use of adhesives or cleaners or accidental spills on the underlay can also result in colour changes in resilient flooring.

Telegraphing of the joints in the underlay through the resilient flooring can be annoying and costly to repair. Builders face the difficult task of matching materials such as subfloor, underlay, joint fillers, adhesives, and finish flooring.

Underlay materials must be acclimatized to the temperature and moisture conditions expected during occupancy of the house. Underlay panels are often very susceptible to moisture and can change dimensions almost overnight. Acclimatizing is a difficult but important step toward minimizing flooring problems.

As ceramic tiles gain widespread acceptance as floor finishes, builders must tackle the problems of providing very sturdy bases upon which to install them. Cracked floor tiles and grout lines are often due to a weak floor structure supporting the tiles or from traffic on the floor before it has properly set or cured.

For lasting beauty, finish flooring requires a properly installed base that utilizes complementary materials and quality installation.

2.3.1 FLOORING MATERIALS
PROBLEM
DISCOLORATION OF RESILIENT FLOORING

CAUSE

Incompatibility of materials

The general consensus to date is that the main cause of discoloration of resilient vinyl flooring is incompatibility of materials. Research suggests that successful installations rely on minimal expansion and subsequent shrinkage of the materials caused by removal of accumulated moisture.

SOLUTIONS

Use recommended underlays with good manufacturers warranty.

◆ There is no evidence yet as to which underlays, if any, cause discoloration of resilient flooring. Some resilient flooring manufacturers have very specific requirements about which products to use. It is best to follow the resilient flooring manufacturer's recommendation for suitable underlays. This is generally a requirement to maintain the warranty on the finish. However most underlay materials can perform properly if attention is paid to certain details.

Use recommended joint fillers.

◆ Resilient flooring manufacturers are usually very specific when they indicate the type of patching compounds that should be used with their products. Follow exactly the underlayment manufacturer's requirements for preparation and installation of the underlay and compatible filler.

Use recommended adhesive.

◆ Resilient flooring manufacturers are usually very specific about the type of adhesive to use with their flooring; they suggest products that they know are compatible. In many cases, they produce adhesive for their flooring. Always follow their recommendations.

Protect underlay from spills.

◆ Many of the tradespeople working in the house use adhesives, solvents, and other similar materials that can damage the underlay if spilled. Even if the spill is immediately cleaned up, the underlay will often absorb some of the spilled material. This material may affect the resilient flooring and sometimes cause show through or yellowing of vinyl.

◆ If spills do occur, clean them up immediately, and repair the affected area: replace the damaged panel, or sand the spill completely and patch the area.

PROBLEM
TELEGRAPHING OF UNDERLAY LEADING TO BUCKLING OF FINISHES

CAUSE

Expansion of underlay from exposure to excessive moisture (for example, curing of freshly poured basement concrete slabs)

SOLUTIONS

Use correct underlay for the location.

◆ Underlay manufacturers recommend specifically where their products should be installed. These recommendations are usually based upon, whatever the moisture conditions are at a site. They do not recommend application of underlay under extreme moisture conditions.

◆ Work should be scheduled near the end of construction. If high moisture is still retained by the subfloor, it should be permitted to dry, or the house should be heated to dry the building materials to more suitable conditions before proceeding.

◆ Most manufacturers require that their underlay be protected from sources of excess heat such as furnaces or hot air ducts. Underlay must also be protected from excess moisture. Installation below grade or above unventilated crawl spaces is generally not recommended except for specific underlay products.

◆ Generally speaking, particleboards and oriented strandboards are more sensitive to heat and moisture changes than plywoods. Closely monitor the use of different underlays in various locations in the house, or take additional steps to seal the resilient flooring to protect it from moisture.

Ensure all edges of resilient flooring are sealed.

◆ Underlays are very susceptible to swelling in areas such as bathrooms and entrances where water either leaks or is tracked in. If joints are not sealed properly, or if flooring edges are not sealed well to the door sill, water can work its way under the resilient flooring and cause the underlay to swell (see Figure 26).

◆ Seal seams in resilient flooring well, and keep traffic away until the adhesive to protect the underlay, is fully cured. Edges of resilient flooring must also be sealed along patio doors where condensation can run down and at door sills, bathtubs, toilets, shower bases, cabinets, vanities, and other locations where water or moisture could be present.

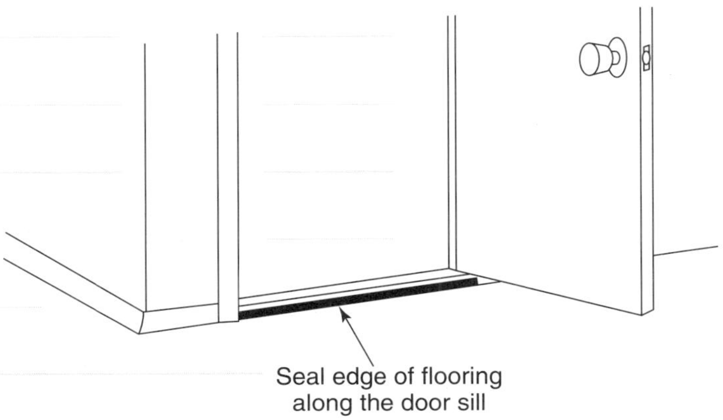

Seal edge of flooring along the door sill

FIGURE 26
EDGE SEALING

◆ Newer types of resilient flooring (known as loose-lay or interflex materials) continue to shrink for many weeks after being installed. It is critical that the edges of this type of flooring be securely fastened to the underlay. As the material shrinks and tightens, sealant used at doorways may pull loose, allowing water to get under the flooring. Check all seals at doorways approximately one month after installing loose-lay resilient flooring, and reseal them if necessary.

Protect and acclimatize underlay before installation, especially where there are extreme temperatures and moisture.

◆ Underlay panels require conditioning or acclimatizing before they are installed. Virtually all underlay manufacturers recommend acclimatization of their product in the house prior to installation. They recommend storing panels flat over three supports in a dry, covered area protected from heat and moisture extremes before, during and after installation. Install panels after they have been allowed to acclimatize to room temperature and humidity, which may take 24–48 hours (depending on local conditions).

Figure 27 demonstrates one method that could be used to acclimatize panels.

◆ Protect underlay from excess moisture, or it may start to swell even before it is installed. Do not store it in a cold, damp garage or on a recently poured slab: this can harm the stability of the underlay panels. If panels are stored outdoors, they must be protected from the elements.

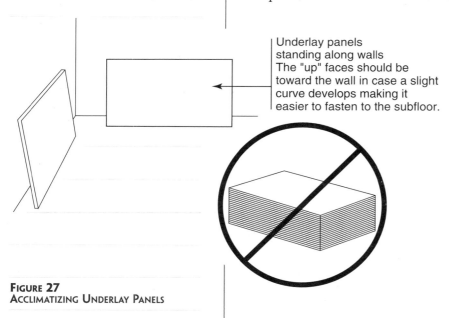

Underlay panels
standing along walls
The "up" faces should be
toward the wall in case a slight
curve develops making it
easier to fasten to the subfloor.

FIGURE 27
ACCLIMATIZING UNDERLAY PANELS

CAUSE

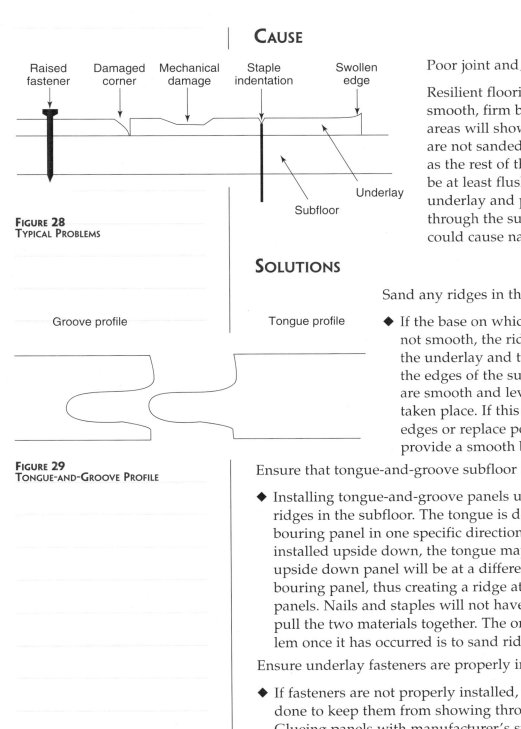

FIGURE 28
TYPICAL PROBLEMS

Raised fastener · Damaged corner · Mechanical damage · Staple indentation · Swollen edge · Underlay · Subfloor

SOLUTIONS

Groove profile   Tongue profile

FIGURE 29
TONGUE-AND-GROOVE PROFILE

Poor joint and/or fastener preparation

Resilient flooring must be installed on a smooth, firm base. High spots and rough areas will show through the finish if they are not sanded smooth to the same level as the rest of the floor. All fasteners must be at least flush with the surface of the underlay and penetrate to just make it through the subfloor or fasteners into joists could cause nail popping (see Figure 28).

Sand any ridges in the subfloor.

◆ If the base on which the underlay is installed is not smooth, the ridges will transfer through the underlay and the resilient flooring. Check the edges of the subfloor to ensure that they are smooth and level, as swelling may have taken place. If this has happened, sand the edges or replace portions of the subfloor to provide a smooth base for the underlay.

Ensure that tongue-and-groove subfloor is installed properly.

◆ Installing tongue-and-groove panels upside down can result in ridges in the subfloor. The tongue is designed to fit into the neighbouring panel in one specific direction (see Figure 29). If a panel is installed upside down, the tongue may fit into the groove, but the upside down panel will be at a different height than the neighbouring panel, thus creating a ridge at the interface of the two panels. Nails and staples will not have enough drawing power to pull the two materials together. The only way to repair this problem once it has occurred is to sand ridges or replace the panel.

Ensure underlay fasteners are properly installed.

◆ If fasteners are not properly installed, there is little that can be done to keep them from showing through the resilient flooring. Glueing panels with manufacturer's suggested adhesive in addition to stapling can help ensure proper fastening. Properly and securely set the fasteners into the underlay panel. Before you install the finish flooring, inspect the underlay and re-set any fasteners that may have lifted. Fasteners are typically countersunk slightly below the surface of the underlay and penetrate just through the subfloor.

◆ Follow underlayment manufacturers fastening recommendations. Some manufacturers and best practise suggests additional fasteners at 50 mm (2-in.) around the perimeter and 100 mm (4-in.) in the field for particle board and 75 mm (3-in.) around the perimeter and 100 mm (4-in.) in the field for plywood. This is dependent on the underlayment thickness.

◆ Place underlay panels perpendicular to the subfloor panels and offset joints to minimize any uneven areas in the subfloor. Panels should be placed with joints lightly butted together, 2 mm (1/16-in.) for particle board and 1 mm (1/32-in.) for plywood.

◆ Install underlay panels with proper fasteners so that the panels do not buckle and the edges do not lift. Generally speaking, the panels should be fastened starting at one corner and fanning out to the other corners. Fully fasten underlay panels when you install them; otherwise buckling may occur. Do not tack the corners first. Leave an 8- to 9-mm (1/4- to 3/8-in.) gap at walls to allow for panel expansion.

Use recommended joint filler as suggested by the underlayment manufacturer.

◆ Only fill joints that are 2 mm (1/16 in.) or greater and allow them to dry thoroughly before applying resilient flooring. Attempting to patch joints that are smaller than 2 mm (1/16 in.) does not allow the filler to bond to the full panel thickness; it then pops out when the underlay expands, causing a ridge in the resilient flooring. If you cannot do a proper job filling the gap to full depth it should be left alone.

◆ The type of joint filler used to fill joints and holes must be compatible with both the resilient flooring and with the underlay. The joint filler should be a hard, quick-setting, non-shrinking patching compound. It should not affect the underlay, particularly the edges of the panel. Use a quality cement-based filler with an acrylic additive. Gypsum-based fillers are not recommended. Manufacturers of resilient flooring have specific requirements and often manufacture their own products. Keep fillers at room temperature. Avoid storing them overnight in cold conditions.

Properly sand and dry all joints and patches.

◆ Properly dry and power-sand smooth joints, fasteners, and other areas whether they have been patched or not. Problems can occur if the patches are sanded and the resilient flooring is applied before the patches have thoroughly dried.

PROBLEM
CERAMIC TILE CRACKING

CAUSE

Inadequate base

Cracking of ceramic tile floors usually occurs in the mortar joint between tiles, although the tiles themselves can also crack. Deflection of the supporting floor system or even vibration of the floor system can cause the cracking to occur. The mortar and the tiles themselves are very rigid and cannot accommodate much movement.

SOLUTIONS

Block subfloor as required.

◆ Minimize the overall movement of the floor system and the deflections between structural members by reducing or eliminating differential movement between subfloor panels. This will help to reduce some of the cracking that can occur in ceramic tile floors.

◆ It is recommended that you install blocking at all panel edges when using either tongue-and-groove subfloor panels or square-edged panels. This will provide a more solid base upon which to install the underlay (see Figure 30).

Use recommended subfloor.

◆ Follow the manufacturers' recommendations. Some manufacturers will not warranty their products if they are installed over oriented strandboard.

Use recommended underlay and recommended thickness.

◆ Your use of a panel-type underlay will depend on whether you use a mortar bed. If the ceramic tiles are installed with adhesive (thin-set method), then underlay as specified in the NBC (see Figure 31). If you use a mortar bed, underlay is not required, although it will help to stiffen the floor and reduce deflection.

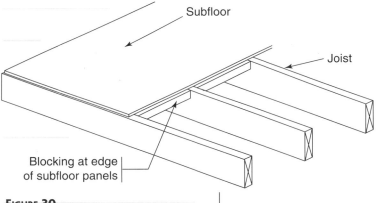

FIGURE 30
PANEL-EDGE BLOCKING

Subfloor

Joist

Blocking at edge of subfloor panels

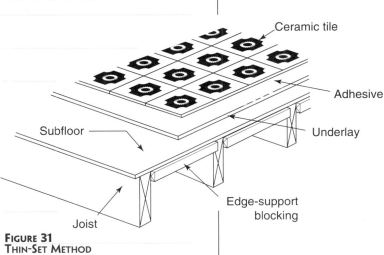

FIGURE 31
THIN-SET METHOD

Ceramic tile

Adhesive

Underlay

Subfloor

Edge-support blocking

Joist

◆ The NBC does not specify the type of underlay material to use. The Terrazo, Tile and Marble Association of Canada recommends using a plywood underlay when tiles are installed using adhesive. It does not recommend using strandboard, waferboard, or particleboard.

◆ The NBC requirements for underlay thicknesses for use with ceramic tiles applied with adhesive are more restrictive than for other floor finishes. The NBC requires the use of 6-mm (1/4-in.) underlay where the supports are spaced up to 300 mm (12 in.) o.c.; and 11-mm (7/16-in.) underlay where the supports are spaced wider than 300 mm (12 in.). The NBC requires that fasteners be spaced not more than 150 mm (6 in.) o.c. along the edges and not more than 200 mm (8 in.) o.c. at other locations.

◆ The Terrazzo, Tile and Marble Association of Canada recommends that underlay be plywood and a minimum thickness of 16 mm (5/8 in.). It also recommends fasteners be spaced not more than 150 mm (6 in.) o.c. along the edges and not more than 300 mm (12 in.) o.c. at other locations.

Use recommended mortar bed.

◆ The NBC recommends that ceramic tiles be set in a mortar bed or be applied to a sound, smooth base with a suitable adhesive.

◆ The Terrazzo, Tile and Marble Association of Canada recommends that, when a mortar bed is used, a polyethylene film be installed over the subfloor followed by a 50 x 50-mm (2 x 2-in.) galvanized wire mesh and then a 32-mm (1-1/4-in.) bed of mortar (see Figure 32).

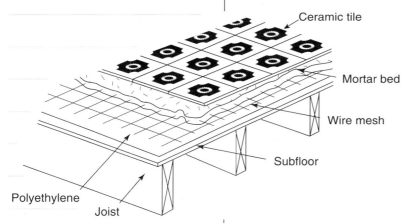

Ceramic tile

Mortar bed

Wire mesh

Subfloor

Polyethylene

Joist

FIGURE 32
CERAMIC TILE SET IN MORTAR BED

CAUSE

Early traffic

Ceramic tile floors are very sensitive to movement immediately after installation. While the mortar bed achieves half of its strength relatively quickly, it is still susceptible to damage due to stresses incurred during the grouting process. During the first 14 days, if people or furniture excessively load a ceramic tile mortar bed, irreparable damage may occur. When tiles are installed using adhesive, the manufacturer's recommendations for curing time must be followed. Tiles can become dislodged if loads are applied too soon. Grout is installed after the tiles are firmly in place and must also be allowed to cure according to the manufacturer's instructions.

SOLUTIONS

Keep traffic off newly installed floor.

◆ If grouting must be done soon after installation of the tile, the installers should use kneeling boards. Take care when moving heavy loads, such as appliances, equipment, or furniture, over a newly installed floor. This may be the largest load ever put on the floor, and it may be applied when the floor is not at its maximum strength, causing cracking even before occupancy.

PROBLEM
CRACKING OF HARDWOOD JOINTS

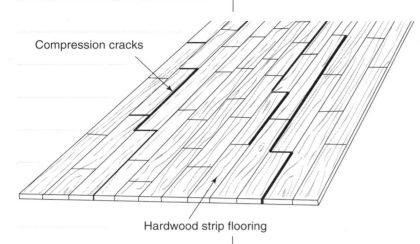

Compression cracks

Hardwood strip flooring

FIGURE 33
COMPRESSION CRACKS

CAUSE

Hardwood swells or shrinks after installation.

Cracks that develop within weeks or months of the installation of a well-laid hardwood floor are usually the result of changes in moisture content. As moisture is absorbed by the hardwood, it expands, pressing neighbouring boards against one another. This pressure crushes the wood fibres, leaving what is known as "compression set." After the hardwood has been compressed in this way, it never completely recovers its original width. When hardwood loses this accumulated moisture, each board shrinks away from the other, leaving cracks that are equal to the amount of crushing or "set" the board underwent (see Figure 33).

SOLUTIONS

If hardwood is dried excessively, it can shrink from its original width and cause similar gaps without the crushing taking place. Once again, cracks can develop between the boards.

Use a moisture barrier under the hardwood.

◆ Wood flooring should be separated from sources of high moisture by a moisture barrier. This is particularly important over areas such as crawl spaces. Installation of polyethylene over the sub-floor prior to installation may prove helpful, and the installation of a ground cover is essential.

◆ If the wood flooring is installed over a source of heat, such as a furnace or uninsulated heating duct, it may dry out and thus shrink. Install insulation above such sources of heat to prevent over-drying of the hardwood floor above.

◆ Allow wood to reach equilibrium before installing it.

PROBLEM
CROWNING OF HARDWOOD BOARDS

CAUSE

Sanding of wet hardwood

Crowning is caused when flooring absorbs moisture on the underside and expands, raising the outside edges of the boards in a cup-like fashion. If the floor is sanded while in this cupped position, the edges of each board will become thinner than the rest of the board. When the boards subsequently dry, the outside edges return to their original positions, which will then be lower than the rest of the board surface (see Figure 34).

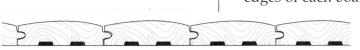

FIGURE 34
CROWNING OF HARDWOOD

SOLUTIONS

Protect wood from changes in humidity.

◆ Wood flooring must be protected from excessive changes in humidity so that its moisture content remains relatively stable. If it is installed over an area of higher humidity, protect it by placing a moisture barrier beneath it.

Allow wood to reach equilibrium before finishing.

◆ Allow the hardwood to reach the moisture content under which it will be in service. Delay sanding and finishing the hardwood until it reaches its equilibrium. Break hardwood material down into small lots, and store the lots in the rooms in which they will be installed. You may need to allow four to five days for the flooring to become acclimatized to the moisture conditions in the house (see Figure 35).

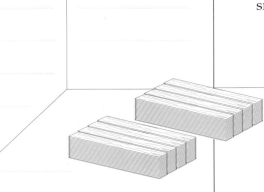

FIGURE 35
ACCLIMATIZING HARDWOOD IN HOUSE

PROBLEM
SQUEAKING HARDWOOD FLOORS

CAUSE

Inadequate subfloor

If the subfloor is inadequate, the hardwood can flex and cause fasteners to loosen. When loose fasteners allow hardwood to move, squeaks soon develop.

SOLUTIONS

Use proper subflooring.

◆ The NBC does not require subflooring if the joist spacing is 400 mm (16 in.) o.c. and the thickness of matched hardwood is not less than 19 mm (3/4 in.). If the joist spacing is up to 600 mm (24 in.) o.c., the NBC requires the subfloor to be not less than 12-mm (1/2-in.) plywood or grade O-2 waferboard or strandboard. Many of the manufacturers of hardwood recommend the use of 16-mm (5/8-in.) or thicker plywood for the subfloor (see Table 1).

Minimum Thickness of Flooring, mm (in.)			
Type of Flooring	Max. Joist Spacing	With Subfloor	Without Subfloor
Matched Hardwood (interior use only)	400 (16)	7.9 (5/16)	19.0 (3/4)
	600 (24)	7.9 (5/16)	33.3 (1-5/16)
Matched Softwood (interior or exterior)	400 (16)	19.0 (3/4)	19.0 (3/4)
	600 (24)	19.0 (3/4)	31.7 (1-1/4)
Squared-edge Softwood (exterior use only)	400 (16)	—	—
	600 (24)	—	38.1 (1-1/2)

Table 1
Thickness of Wood Strip Flooring

◆ A good grade of asphalt felt or building paper is often installed under the hardwood. This is designed to keep out the dust and to reduce the movement of moisture from below (see Figure 36).

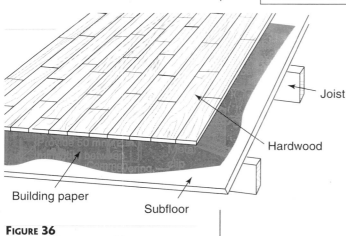

Joist

Hardwood

Building paper

Subfloor

FIGURE 36
BUILDING PAPER UNDER HARDWOOD

PROBLEM
SQUEAKING

CAUSE

Inadequate fasteners

Inadequate fasteners allow the hardwood strips to flex and thus squeak against one another.

SOLUTIONS

Use proper nails or staples.

◆ The NBC requires wood-strip flooring to be either nailed or stapled, depending upon the thickness of the flooring. Staples can only be used to fasten strip flooring that is not more than 8 mm (5/16 in.) thick. Proper nail length and spacing depends upon the thickness of the finish flooring (see Table 2).

Nailing of Wood Strip Flooring, mm (in.)		
Finish Flooring Thickness	Minimum Length of Flooring Nails	Maximum Spacing of Flooring Nails
7.9 (5/16)	38 (1-1/2)	200 (8)
11.1 (7/16)	51 (2)	300 (12)
19.0 (3/4)	57 (2-1/4)	400 (16)
25.4 (1)	63 (2-1/2)	400 (16)
31.7 (1-1/4)	70 (2-3/4)	600 (24)
38.1 (1-1/2)	83 (3-1/4)	600 (24)

Table 2
Nailing Requirements for Wood Strip Flooring

Section 2.4 Additional Reading

SOURCE	PUBLICATION
Canada Mortgage and Housing Corporation Canadian Housing Information Centre 700 Montreal Road Ottawa ON K1A 0P7 613 748-2367	*Canadian Wood-Frame House Construction*, 1997 NHA 5031
Canadian Wood Council 1400 Blair Place, Suite 210 Ottawa ON K1J 9B8 613 747-5544	*The Span Book*, 1995 *Introduction to Wood Building Technology*, 1997
National Research Council of Canada Institute for Research in Construction Publications Section Ottawa ON K1A 0R6 In Ottawa: 613 993-2463 Other locations: 1 800 672-7990	*The Difference Between a Vapour Barrier and an Air Barrier*, 1985 BPN 54 *Humidity, Condensation, Ventilation in Houses*, 1984 NRCC 23293 *Decay of Wood*, 1969 CBD 111 *Vapour Barriers: What Are They? Are They Effective?* 1976 CBD 176 *Moisture Problems in Houses*, 1984 CBD 231 *Effects of Wood Shrinkage in Buildings*, 1984 CBD 231
Ontario New Home Warranty Program 5160 Yonge Street, 6th Floor North York ON M2N 6L9 416 229-9200	*Building Successful Floor Systems*, 1994 ISBN 1-895389-39-9

CHAPTER 3
Introduction

WALL SYSTEMS

This chapter presents all aspects of wall systems, from the outside cladding through to the inside finish...and everything in between. It highlights the prevalent wall systems problems in new Canadian housing, clarifies the most common causes of these problems, and identifies design and construction practices that are likely to reduce the incidence of construction defects and customer callbacks. While not exhaustive, this chapter does address the more common construction practices in use across the country.

Moisture is the primary source of construction problems. Rain and snow leaking into wall cavities, moisture escaping from the inside of the home, and even the moisture resident in framing lumber can create a host of problems ranging from structural failure to the deterioration of cladding and interior finishes.

Good design and construction practices can eliminate these problems. Proper installation of the exterior cladding, and the use of drier lumber and an effective air barrier system are all described in this chapter. Share the information with your designers, your site managers, and your sub-contractors. Improved practices will result in a more durable, better-performing wall system—free from costly callbacks, which can stress your bank account and your relationship with your customers.

Section 3.1 Moisture and Wall Systems
INTRODUCTION

Directly or indirectly, moisture is the single greatest source of construction defects in wall systems. These defects can be the result of

◆ changing moisture levels in framing materials;

◆ the movement of vapour-laden house air through the envelope; and

◆ the movement of external moisture into the building cladding systems.

These factors might cause structural failure, the deterioration and decay of wall assembly components, visual and aesthetic problems, and poor performance of the building's thermal envelope.

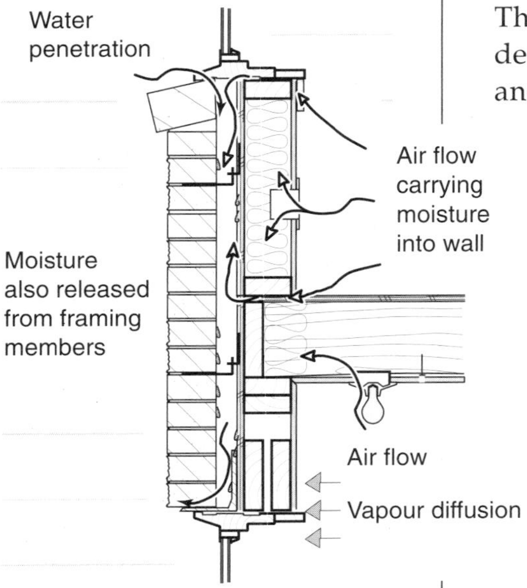

Water penetration

Air flow carrying moisture into wall

Moisture also released from framing members

Air flow

Vapour diffusion

FIGURE 1
MOISTURE-RELATED FACTORS INFLUENCING WALL SYSTEMS

3.1.1 MOISTURE AND WOOD

Water is present in large quantities in trees and in freshly cut (green) lumber. In some species of wood used in construction, the moisture content can be as high as 100 percent—meaning that the weight of the water in the wood is equivalent to the weight of the wood when it is completely dried.

As wood seasons, its moisture content decreases. Dry wood, as required by the National Building Code of Canada (NBC), is defined as wood having a moisture content of 19 percent or less. Wood containing more than 19 percent moisture is called green lumber.

The Equilibrium Moisture Content (EMC) in lumber refers to the point at which the moisture content in the lumber stabilizes. After a period of not more than one year, properly installed framing lumber will reach a moisture content of 7 to 10 percent. Wall drying test research performed in the Atlantic provinces and Ontario has demonstrated that the rate of lumber drying is affected by both the temperature of the cavity and by the permeability of the exterior sheathing.

As the framing lumber dries after installation, you must address several concerns, including

◆ dimensional changes (shrinkage, twisting, bowing, and cupping) of the lumber; and

◆ decay of the lumber where moisture is trapped in the wall assembly.

PROBLEM
DIMENSIONAL CHANGES

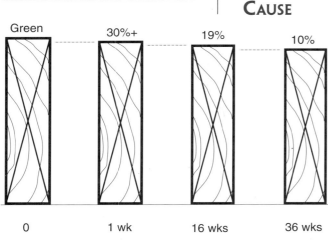

FIGURE 2
SHRINKAGE VS. MOISTURE CONTENT FOR KILN-DRIED LUMBER

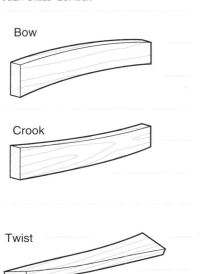

FIGURE 3
INTERNAL STRESSES IN WOOD

CAUSE

Swelling and shrinkage as moisture enters and leaves the wood

When wood is dried from the fibre saturation point to 19 percent average moisture content, lumber shrinks about 2.35 percent in width. On a board measuring 235 mm (9-1/2 in.) wide, this would result in shrinkage of 6 mm (1/4 in.). As lumber continues to dry to 7 to 10 percent, some further shrinkage will occur, most noticeably at floor headers (see Figure 2).

Drying has little effect on the length of the lumber. However, as the wood dries out, internal stresses are created. These stresses can result in the wood's bowing (crowning), crooking, twisting, or cupping (see Figure 3).

SOLUTIONS

◆ Schedule lumber deliveries to minimize the time lumber is stored on site.

◆ Keep lumber off the ground, away from free-standing water, snow, or curing concrete slabs.

◆ Maintain wrappings on lumber for as long as possible, or cover lumber with a tarpaulin to protect it from rain and snow.

◆ Store the lumber flat, with sufficient supports; wood tends to take a permanent set when deformed for long periods of time.

◆ Promote ventilation of piles of lumber by keeping piles separated with spacers between lumber layers.

◆ Restrain thin or long pieces of wood in piles by packaging these or weighting them down; thin pieces will deform more than thick pieces, and long pieces are more likely to deform than short pieces.

◆ If wood must be stored on end, provide sufficient supports and rotate the pieces end-over-end periodically.

PROBLEM
DECAY CAUSED BY CONDENSATION

CAUSE

Fungal growth in the cell walls of wood

Fungal growth will occur when moisture is present between the temperatures of 20 and 30°C (68 and 86°F).

SOLUTIONS

Provide a moisture-free environment.

Since you can exert little control over the temperature and supply of air in cavities, the best way to prevent decay is to provide a moisture-free environment for it. Most fungi cannot reproduce when the moisture content of wood is less than 19 percent.

3.1.2 MOISTURE AND AIR LEAKAGE

PROBLEM

THE MOVEMENT OF WARM, VAPOUR-LADEN AIR THROUGH THE WALL SYSTEM IN WINTER

CAUSE

Pressure differences between the interior and exterior of the building

Winds, the stack effect, and mechanical systems can all induce pressure differences between the interior of the building and its exterior. Inside air can be driven by these pressures through leaks and cracks in the air barrier system of the dwelling. While some vapour also moves via vapour diffusion pressures, air leakage is responsible for more than 99 percent of the moisture movement into the wall cavities.

When the water vapour comes into contact with cooler surfaces inside the wall assembly, the vapour can condense; often it is visible in the form of frost on the back of sheathing. Vapour that condenses inside the wall cavity as water can promote fungal growth, deteriorate wood framing members, lead to corrosion of fasteners in the wall system, and lead to deterioration of the cladding system (cracking of brick, buckling of painted surfaces, cracking of stucco, etc.) (see Figure 4).

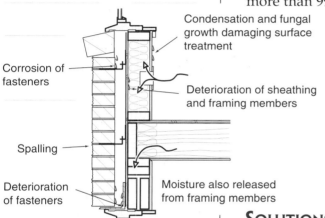

Condensation and fungal growth damaging surface treatment

Corrosion of fasteners

Deterioration of sheathing and framing members

Spalling

Deterioration of fasteners

Moisture also released from framing members

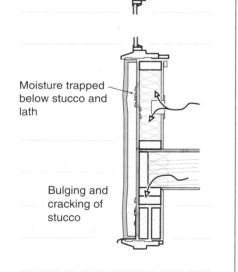

Moisture trapped below stucco and lath

Bulging and cracking of stucco

FIGURE 4
POTENTIAL MOISTURE PROBLEM RELATING TO AIR LEAKAGES

SOLUTIONS

Provide an effective air-barrier system.

Of primary importance to the long-term durability of walls is the provision of an effective air-barrier system that prevents the movement of moisture inside the house into the cavity.

◆ Ensure that the air-barrier system is continuous throughout the building envelope, free of leakage openings, and sealed at all penetrations in the envelope.

◆ Structurally support the air-barrier system to reduce deflection, cracking, or movement resulting in the breaking of seals and the deterioration of the air barrier over time.

◆ Constuct the air-barrier system with materials that have a high resistance to the flow of air.

◆ When the air-barrier system is installed in a location where condensation might occur, ensure that it permits the passage of water vapour. Materials should have a vapour permeability of greater than 60 ng/(Pa•s•m^2)(1.04 grains/[ft^2•s•in.Hg.]).

◆ Where the air barrier comprises materials with a low water vapour permeability (polyethylene, aluminum foil, etc.), generally position the air barrier on the warm side of the insulation.

Recommended detailing for air barrier systems is provided in The Details of Air Barrier Systems in Houses, *published by the Ontario New Home Warranty Program.*

3.1.3 EXTERNAL MOISTURE PROBLEM

RAIN AND SNOW PENETRATION INTO BUILDING CLADDING SYSTEMS

CAUSE

Openings

When openings are available, and when there are sufficient pressures to drive the water into the assembly, rain and snow will enter the building cladding systems.

SOLUTIONS

Apply proper flashings and sealants.

◆ These represent the first line of defence.

Protect wall sheathing with properly installed sheathing paper.

◆ Apply this solution if you do not install face-sealed cladding systems.

Control the driving forces in the design.

◆ Despite the design of wider roof overhangs and cantilevered projections, walls will still be wetted during rain storms accompanied by driving winds. Even good quality exterior caulkings and sealants can develop cracks over time as materials age and building elements shift. Eventually, water will enter through those cracks.

◆ If the driving forces are controlled and accommodated in the design, rain penetration can be effectively controlled. Water entry from capillary suction, gravity, and air pressure differences can be effectively controlled through rain-screen design principles. Through the introduction of an air space behind the cladding (or joint), air pressure behind the cladding can equal that on the face of the wall, eliminating the driving force responsible for causing water to move inward.

Install a rain-screen wall.

◆ A rain-screen wall consists of an outer layer of siding or cladding, and an inner wall separated by an air space (see Figure 5). The air cavity must be vented to the outside to allow pressure equalization and must be equipped with drains at the bottom of the cavity to remove any moisture which accumulates in the cavity. To perform effectively, the rain-screen design requires an effective air-barrier system within the building envelope (either at the inner face of the wall or as a component of the exterior sheathing).

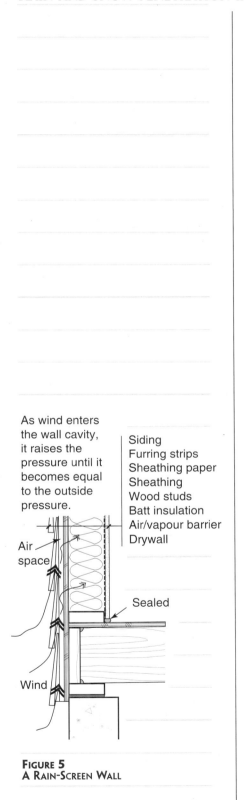

As wind enters the wall cavity, it raises the pressure until it becomes equal to the outside pressure.

Siding
Furring strips
Sheathing paper
Sheathing
Wood studs
Batt insulation
Air/vapour barrier
Drywall

Air space

Sealed

Wind

FIGURE 5
A RAIN-SCREEN WALL

Several requirements must be met in the design of a rain-screen wall to ensure effective long-term performance:

◆ If the wall assembly is not airtight, pressure equalization will not occur, resulting in water being driven into the wall.

◆ The air space behind the cladding must be contained at the top of the wall and at corners to maintain pressure equalization (see Figure 6).

◆ Openings must be provided on the face of the exterior wall to permit air to enter the cavity.

◆ Sheathing paper, flashings, and drains must be provided to direct water out of the air space (see Figure 7).

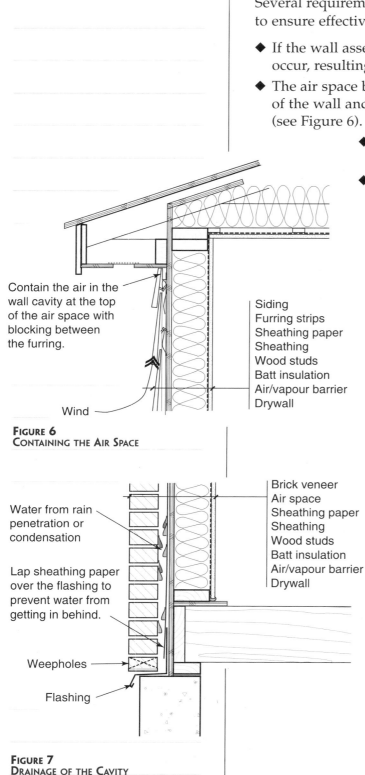

Contain the air in the wall cavity at the top of the air space with blocking between the furring.

Siding
Furring strips
Sheathing paper
Sheathing
Wood studs
Batt insulation
Air/vapour barrier
Drywall

Wind

FIGURE 6
CONTAINING THE AIR SPACE

Water from rain penetration or condensation

Lap sheathing paper over the flashing to prevent water from getting in behind.

Brick veneer
Air space
Sheathing paper
Sheathing
Wood studs
Batt insulation
Air/vapour barrier
Drywall

Weepholes

Flashing

FIGURE 7
DRAINAGE OF THE CAVITY

Section 3.2 Framing Problems
INTRODUCTION

In a wood-frame house, wall framing includes studs, plates, blocking and strapping, interior partitions, and wall sheathing.

Also included are framing members around openings, jack studs, cripples, and lintels.

Most homes in Canada have walls that are platform-framed, resting on the floor system below and supporting the floor system above. In some instances, balloon-framing is still used where wall framing is continuous over a number of floors, without interruption at floors (see Figure 8).

Platform frame

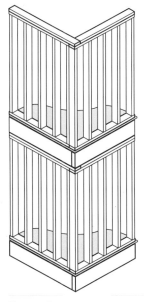

Balloon frame

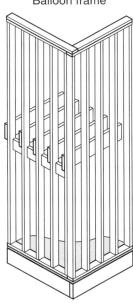

FIGURE 8
FRAMING METHODS

3.2.1 STRUCTURAL DETERIORATION
PROBLEM
STRUCTURAL DETERIORATION OF WALL-FRAMING MEMBERS AND SHEATHING

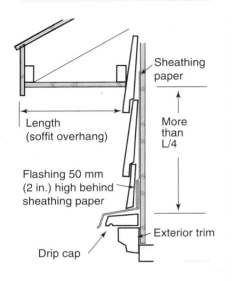

Length (soffit overhang)

Sheathing paper

More than L/4

Flashing 50 mm (2 in.) high behind sheathing paper

Drip cap

Exterior trim

FIGURE 9
FLASHING DETAIL

CAUSE

Moisture in the wall cavity

Moisture can accumulate in the wall cavity when it is driven through the exterior cladding sytems, or it can result from leakage of vapour-laden air from the interior of the building. When proper construction techniques are used, this type of construction can be durable and defect-free. However, when poor construction techniques are applied, wall framing and sheathing can be subject to fungal attack and decay.

SOLUTIONS

Control rain penetration.

◆ Ensure that flashings are installed to direct water away from the face of the wall around all openings (see Figure 9).

◆ Ensure that effective rain-screen principles are incorporated into the design of the exterior cladding (as discussed in section 3.1.3). These should include

  – an effective air-barrier system;

  – drainage and venting of the cavity; and

  – compartmentalization of the wall cavities.

Prevent the flow of humid interior air into the wall cavity.

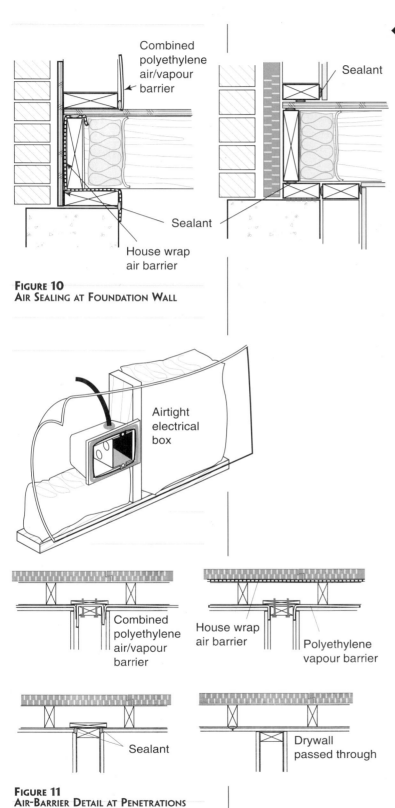

Combined
polyethylene
air/vapour
barrier

Sealant

Sealant

House wrap
air barrier

FIGURE 10
AIR SEALING AT FOUNDATION WALL

Airtight
electrical
box

Combined
polyethylene
air/vapour
barrier

House wrap
air barrier

Polyethylene
vapour barrier

Sealant

Drywall
passed through

FIGURE 11
**AIR-BARRIER DETAIL AT PENETRATIONS
AND INTERSECTING PARTITIONS**

◆ Install an airtight barrier in the wall structure. Ensure that the air barrier system is continuous through all components of the envelope, minimizing the potential for air flow around windows and doors, around electrical outlets at floor and partition wall assemblies, and where electrical and plumbing systems are routed from the exterior wall to interior partitions. Air-barrier systems must be continuous, structurally supported, resistant to air flow, durable, and easy to maintain over time (see Figures 10 and 11).

3.2.2 MOISTURE AND WOOD

PROBLEM
WALL DEFORMATION CAUSED BY SHRINKAGE

As framing lumber dries, it shrinks and undergoes internal stresses that cause the wood members to warp, bow, cup, twist, and check. Other symptoms of lumber drying are nail pops and drywall cracks.

CAUSE

Wet lumber

Lumber can be excessively wet, either as purchased from the lumber supplier, or as a result of poor site storage and handling procedures. The generation of excessive moisture during the construction phases (drying of concrete, drywall mud, paint, and moisture from temporary heating sources), can also increase the moisture loading in the framing lumber.

SOLUTIONS

Improve purchasing procedures.

◆ Specify dry lumber with a moisture content not greater than 19 percent from your suppliers. Many lumberyards have lumber with very high moisture content. Select lumber carefully.

Improve site storage and handling of lumber as discussed in section 3.1.1.

Minimize extreme moisture generation during the construction phase.

◆ Avoid generating excessive moisture during construction by
 – providing as much natural and mechanical ventilation as possible during construction; and
 – avoiding the use of unvented propane or gas heaters during winter.

Implement corrective measures to ensure the frame is straight.

◆ Inspect the framing after it has been constructed to determine whether it is level, plumb, and true. Use the following steps to correct problems:
 – Straighten bowed studs (crowns) by saw-cutting the concave or hollow sides and driving in wedges; provide nailing scabs to reinforce the cut stud (see Figure 12).
 – Provide blocking between studs that bow sideways (Figure 13).
 – Although studs shrink very little in length, check that they all reach the top plates. If they do not, install hardwood shims to fill the space (do not use cedar shims—they are easily crushed and do not provide adequate bearing strength).

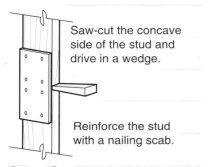

Saw-cut the concave side of the stud and drive in a wedge.

Reinforce the stud with a nailing scab.

FIGURE 12
STRAIGHTENING WARPED STUDS

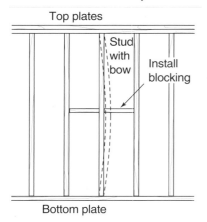

Top plates

Stud with bow

Install blocking

Bottom plate

FIGURE 13
PREVENTING OR CORRECTING "BOWING"

PROBLEM
WEAKENED WALL STUDS

Weakened studs can result in distortion of the frame and cracked surface finishes.

CAUSE

Poor installation procedures resulting in studs being out of plumb, or weakening through excessive notching and drilling of bearing studs

SOLUTIONS

Install studs plumb.

◆ Take care to align studs square. Measure the diagonals of the framing to ensure that the dimensions are equal before lifting it into place. Install a metal brace at 45 degrees let into the studs, or install wall sheathing before erecting the walls.

Notching and drilling of bearing studs should not exceed allowable depth.

◆ Notches, chases, holes, and other penetrations through bearing studs are often required for electrical, plumbing, or heating installations. Notches should not exceed one third of the depth of the stud where it is load-bearing (see Figure 14).

◆ Where notches exceed allowable depth, reinforce them with 38-mm (1-1/2-in.) lumber nailed to the side of the studs and extending 600 mm (24 in.) on each side of the notch or hole.

◆ Reinforce notched top plates in the same fashion if less than 50 mm (2 in.) in width remains (see Figure 15).

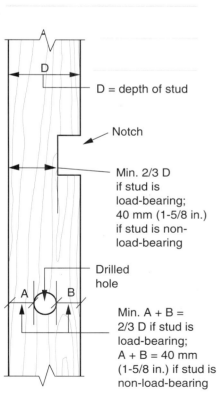

FIGURE 14
NOTCHING OF WALL STUDS

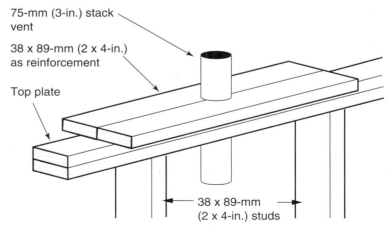

FIGURE 15
NOTCHING OF TOP PLATE

PROBLEM

COLD INTERIOR SURFACES PROMOTING CONDENSATION AND GROWTH OF MOLDS AND MILDEW

CAUSE

Thermal bridging across solid elements of the wall assembly

Thermal bridging occurs when there is a direct path for heat flow from the interior of the building to the exterior. Exterior wall studs and plates encourage the transmission of heat through walls and can promote localized condensation, mildew growth, and dust marking. Less noticeable will be increased conductive heat losses, higher energy bills, and diminished occupant comfort. Thermal bridging will be most noticeable where framing members are concentrated—such as at corners.

Reduce the amount of lumber used in wall framing, or provide a thermal break in the wall system.

SOLUTIONS

◆ Use the maximum stud spacing permitted by the NBC to reduce the number of studs, which are responsible for thermal bridging (see Figure 16). Stud spacing must accommodate NBC requirements for fastening and thickness of exterior sheathing and cladding.

◆ Reduce the number of framing members used in corner and partition intersection details. Use nailing clips to support drywall or exterior sheet materials (see Figure 17).

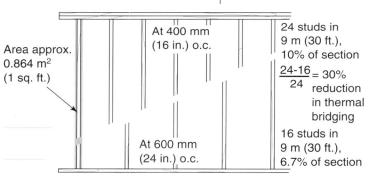

Area approx. 0.864 m² (1 sq. ft.)

At 400 mm (16 in.) o.c.

At 600 mm (24 in.) o.c.

24 studs in 9 m (30 ft.), 10% of section

$$\frac{24-16}{24} = 30\%$$ reduction in thermal bridging

16 studs in 9 m (30 ft.), 6.7% of section

FIGURE 16
PERCENTAGE OF STUD SURFACE IN WALL SECTION

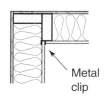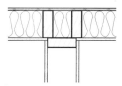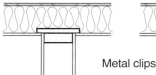

Studs

Metal clip

Metal clips

FIGURE 17
EXTERIOR WALL AND INTERIOR PARTITION INTERSECTION

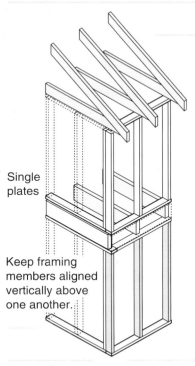

Single plates

Keep framing members aligned vertically above one another.

FIGURE 18
ALIGNED FRAMING MEMBERS

◆ Use single top-plates where the design allows for floor joists and trusses to be directly located over the stud below (see Figure 18).

◆ In load-bearing exterior walls, fabricate structural box beams to serve as headers over doors and windows. The use of structural sheathing on both sides of the framing allows for the incorporation of higher levels of insulation at headers (see Figure 19).

◆ Use exterior insulated sheathing to provide a thermal break for the framing. Many builders now install exterior insulated sheathing between the exterior wall frame and the exterior finish to provide an additional thermal break.

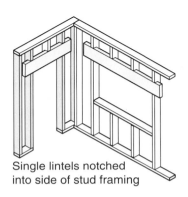

Single lintels notched into side of stud framing

FIGURE 19
REDUCED HEADER

Section 3.3 Windows and Doors

INTRODUCTION

Windows and doors are two of the most vulnerable elements of the wall system. Not only do they represent the only "moving parts" of the system, but they are subjected to greater temperature differentials than other elements of the wall assembly.

Manufacturers claim that as many as 50 percent of all callbacks relating to windows and doors in new housing could be avoided through better installation practices. This section of the guide identifies the causes and solutions to problems typically witnessed in new housing.

3.3.1 OPERATING PROBLEMS
PROBLEM
DIFFICULTY IN OPERATING A DOOR OR WINDOW

Doors that bind, sliders that don't slide, and windows that won't open or close properly are common sources of warranty complaints. They are often indications of poor framing and installation practices.

CAUSE

Insufficient tolerances

Installation must be able to accommodate building movement, out-of-squareness, and differential shrinkage of rough framing and door and window frames.

SOLUTIONS

◆ Ensure that framing is square by measuring diagonals and installing bracing before you erect walls.

◆ Ensure that rough openings are at least 12 mm (1/2 in.) wider and 12 mm (1/2 in.) higher than the window or door frame size. Some manufacturers recommend 40 mm and 20 mm (1-1/2 in. and 3/4 in.) respectively (see Figure 20).

◆ Use pre-hung doors, or hang doors with at least a 3-mm (1/8-in.) clearance on tops and sides (see Figure 21). Secure top hinges with long screws to prevent sagging.

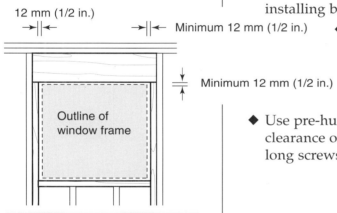

FIGURE 20
ROUGH WINDOW OPENING

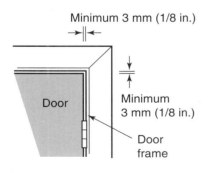

FIGURE 21
HANGING CLEARANCES

PROBLEM
DIFFICULTY IN OPERATING WINDOWS OR DOORS

CAUSE

Deflection or rotation of lintel

Windows and doors are not designed to support vertical loads from other elements of the wall system.

SOLUTIONS

◆ Avoid eccentric loads on lintels. Ensure adequate lintel strength and full bearing on jack studs. Make sure that jack studs are square. Limit lintel deflection to 1/360 of the span — for example, 5 mm (1/4 in.) for a 1.8-m (6-ft.) opening.

◆ Avoid using shims between the frame head and lintel to prevent loads from being transferred to the frame of the window or door. Shims should be used only at the frame jambs and sill. Any anchoring at the head should be with flexible straps to allow some spring action (see Figure 22).

◆ Avoid nailing through the brick-mould into the lintel.

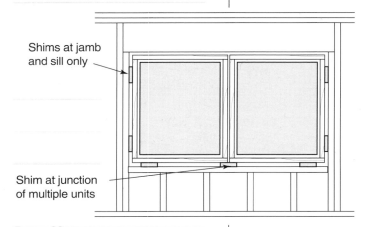

Shims at jamb and sill only

Shim at junction of multiple units

FIGURE 22
SHIM POSITIONS

PROBLEM
DIFFICULTY IN OPERATING WINDOWS OR DOORS

Window frame

Compressive
foam gasket

Caulking

3-mm (1/8-in.) gap

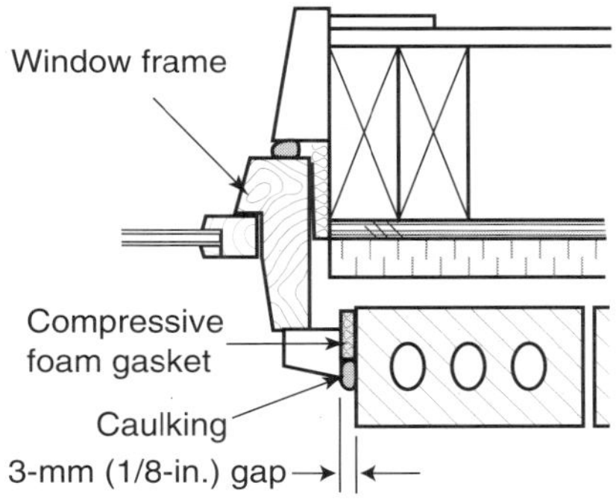

FIGURE 23
DETAIL AT BRICK VENEER

CAUSE

Warpage or distortion of frame

SOLUTIONS

◆ Allow a minimum clearance of 3 mm (1/8 in.) between gypsum board and the window and door frames to minimize pressures on the frames. Avoid cutting back board after installation as this may damage sheet air-barriers.

◆ Avoid distortion caused by unequal pressure around the frame by using precut cedar-shingle shims rather than scrap, and by spacing shims evenly.

◆ When using expansive foam to air seal around the frame, do not overfill the gap that could exert pressures on the frame. Use one-component foams. Remember that the warmer the temperature, the greater the expansion.

◆ Units are less likely to warp after installation if they are stored in conditions similar to those in the building they will be installed in. Avoid exterior storage.

◆ Brick expands with moisture absorption while framing shrinks. Leave a 3-mm (1/8-in.) gap at the sides of the frame, 6 mm (1/4 in.) under the sill and 10 mm (3/8 in.) under second-storey sills. If a sloped brick sill is used, allow additional space under the window. Caulk all gaps and back caulking with a compressive foam gasket (see Figure 23).

◆ Exterior sheathing can expand or warp with exposure to rain and sun. Set sheathing back from the rough opening. Flash openings properly.

◆ Use pre-finished windows, or protect wood frames from absorbing moisture by painting or finishing them shortly after installing them.

◆ Some builders apply sheathing paper or polyethylene in strips over all sides of the rough openings to prevent wall moisture from reaching the window or door frames. Expandable foams or sill gaskets can provide similar characteristics with improved air leakage performance.

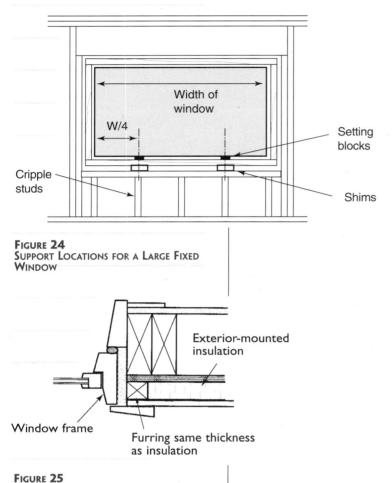

FIGURE 24
SUPPORT LOCATIONS FOR A LARGE FIXED WINDOW

FIGURE 25
EXTERIOR INSULATION DETAIL

◆ To prevent downward sagging of the window frame, align shims and cripple studs with the setting blocks, if possible. Setting blocks are usually located at the quarter points in fixed units, and below the junctions of multiple units (see Figure 24).

◆ Where exterior rigid insulation is used, install a furring strip the same thickness as the insulation around the perimeter of door or window frames to provide adequate surfaces for fastening (see Figure 25). This also provides better backing for caulking and flashing.

PROBLEM

DIFFICULTY IN OPERATING WINDOWS OR DOORS

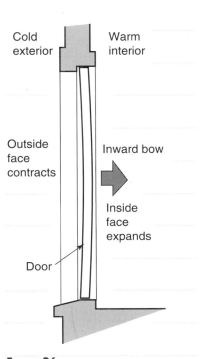

Cold exterior

Warm interior

Outside face contracts

Inward bow

Inside face expands

Door

FIGURE 26
THERMAL BOW

CAUSE

Thermal bow

In colder climates, the temperature differential from the exterior to the interior face of an exterior metal door can cause the door to warp and, in extreme cases, to even pop open in winter. While some bowing is inevitable, it should not interfere with the weathertightness or operation of the door (see Figure 26).

SOLUTIONS

◆ Attach a spacer to the door jamb at the lock to allow for some bowing.
◆ Use in-the-jamb weatherstripping.
◆ Install storm doors or windows in winter to reduce temperature differential.
◆ Dead bolts may provide greater resistance to doors popping open.

CAUSE

Warpage of wood doors

SOLUTIONS

◆ Concrete pouring, drywall finishing, and painting can cause high humidity levels. Provide ventilation during construction.
◆ Store doors flat unless they are prehung.
◆ Delay painting of exterior wood doors until the moisture content of the wood has stabilized. Seal the bottoms and tops of the doors to prevent moisture absorption.

PROBLEM

DIFFICULTY IN OPERATING WINDOWS OR DOORS

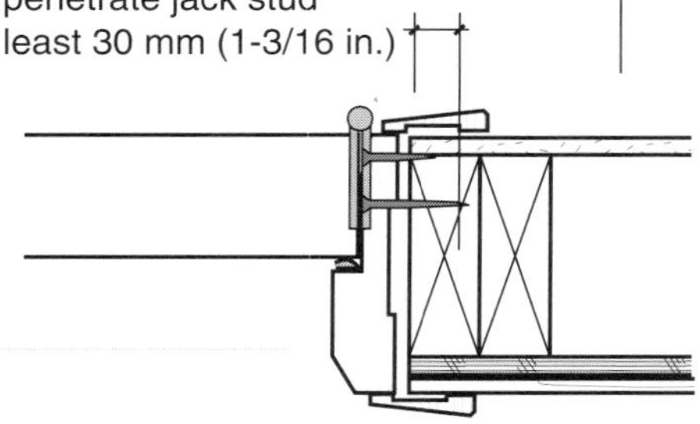

Two screws per hinge
to penetrate jack stud
at least 30 mm (1-3/16 in.)

FIGURE 27
HINGE DETAIL

CAUSE

Inadequate fastening and support of doors

SOLUTIONS

◆ Use shims at all hinge and hardware locations.
◆ At least two screws per hinge should pass through both the frame and the shim and penetrate at least 30 mm (1-3/16 in.) into solid wood (see Figure 27).
◆ Don't drive screws with a hammer.
◆ Consider using heavier-gauge ball-bearing hinges for wider exterior doors.

CAUSE

Lack of final adjustment

SOLUTIONS

◆ Slide operable sash and patio doors back and forth during installation to ensure they remain operable.
◆ Check installation by removing and remounting all removable sashes and screens prior to completion.
◆ Screw door frames through shims to jack studs instead of nailing them, in order to permit later adjustment.
◆ Avoid painting tracks and other vinyl components in sliding doors and windows.
◆ Pre-drill window frames to allow for screwing and future adjustments.

Section 3.4 Siding and Cladding Problems
INTRODUCTION

Siding and cladding defects and failures range from wide-scale deterioration of siding materials through to less destructive, but equally annoying, unsightly appearances. Problems are generally the result of inadequate control of moisture or poor installation techniques. This section of the guide provides the builder with a diagnosis of the most common siding problems and offers suggestions for reducing the likelihood of their recurrence.

3.4.1 GENERIC PROBLEMS

PROBLEM
WATER PENETRATION THROUGH SIDING

Water can penetrate all siding. Trapped moisture can cause rotting, peeling paint, water stains, mold and mildew, damaged insulation, warping and buckling, and severe damage to the wall structure. Water penetrating all the way through the assembly can damage interior finishes.

CAUSE

Lack of a rain-screen wall
Incorrect installation of sheathing paper

SOLUTIONS

◆ Use rain-screen principles to reduce the pressure difference between the exterior (wind) and the interior of the wall and therefore reduce the amount of water moving into the wall cavity (see section 3.1.3). Ensure effective drainage of the wall cavity (see Figure 28).

◆ Make sure that the wall sheathing paper is properly applied, with no rips or tears, and with appropriate overlap of the top sheet over the bottom sheet. The absence of a sheathing membrane or improper installation allows water that has penetrated the exterior siding to move through the wall cavity. Wall sheathing-paper acts as a secondary moisture barrier behind the siding. It should be moisture-resistant but not vapour-resistant, so that water vapour can pass through the wall to the exterior. Apply the following rules:

– One layer of sheathing paper over wall sheathing will be adequate in most instances. Some builders recommend the use of two layers of sheathing paper under stucco cladding. Tar-saturated felts or papers must not be installed as sheathing paper beneath stucco.

– Lap joints in the sheathing paper by a minimum of 100 mm (4 in.). Ensure that the installation of sheathing paper around openings promotes positive drainage down the wall and to the exterior over the flashing (see section 3.4.5).

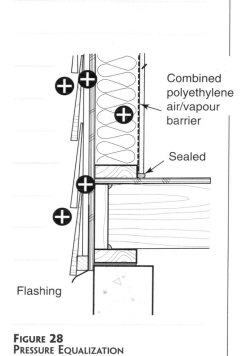

Combined polyethylene air/vapour barrier

Sealed

Flashing

FIGURE 28
PRESSURE EQUALIZATION

PROBLEM
PREMATURE DETERIORATION

Siding can deteriorate prematurely when moisture is present in the wall assembly. Fungi destroy wood fibres and promote the corrosion of metal siding and fasteners.

CAUSE

Condensation resulting from air leakage
Inadequate drying potential

SOLUTIONS

◆ Prevent the flow of warm, humid air into the exterior wall, where it can condense on the back face of cooler siding. Install an effective, continuous air-barrier system to minimize the flow of any airborne water vapour.
◆ Provide a vapour barrier on the warm side of the wall assembly.

PROBLEM
SIDING DEFORMATION OR DISPLACEMENT

Persistent deformation will weaken siding and provide openings through which water can penetrate.

CAUSE

Direct installation over semi-rigid insulation

SOLUTIONS

◆ Provide a stable backing for siding. Siding applied directly over semi-rigid insulation may deform and appear wavy because the insulation compresses when siding is installed too tightly. Use wall sheathing, strapping, or furring for wood and hardboard siding. Use a backing that provides continuous support for vinyl and light metal siding. Heavier metals resist bending and may be spanned over furring strips. It is important to follow the manufacturer's instructions closely.

Buckling at floor header assemblies.

◆ Shrinkage of header and trimmer joists can cause siding to deflect at the floor assemblies. Provide extra clearance at intersections, and allow for the movement of siding installed above and below the assembly.

3.4.2 WOOD AND HARDBOARD SIDING
PROBLEM
WATER PENETRATION THROUGH WOOD AND HARDBOARD SIDING

Water can penetrate through gaps in wood and hardboard siding, causing wood rot, peeling paint, water stains, mold and mildew, damaged insulation, warping and buckling, and severe damage to the wall structure.

CAUSE

The presence of gaps in the siding and incorrect joint construction

SOLUTIONS

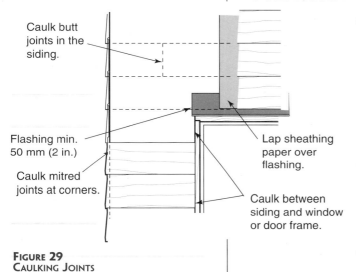

Caulk butt joints in the siding.

Flashing min. 50 mm (2 in.)

Caulk mitred joints at corners.

Lap sheathing paper over flashing.

Caulk between siding and window or door frame.

FIGURE 29
CAULKING JOINTS

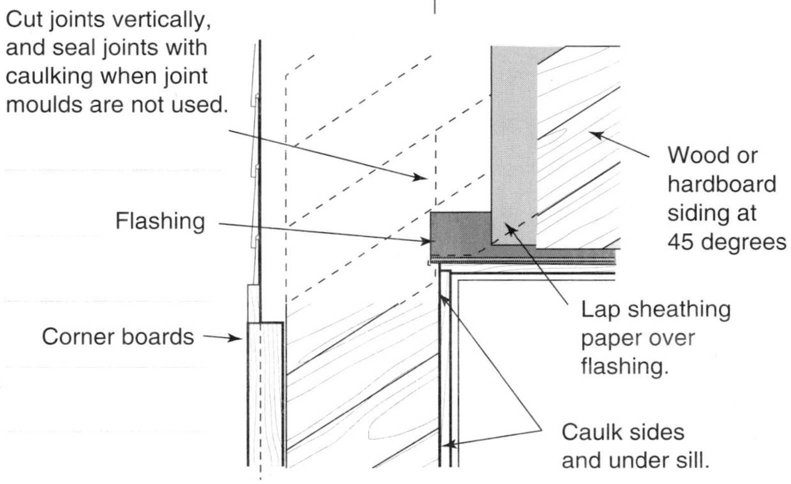

Cut joints vertically, and seal joints with caulking when joint moulds are not used.

Flashing

Corner boards

Wood or hardboard siding at 45 degrees

Lap sheathing paper over flashing.

Caulk sides and under sill.

FIGURE 30
DIAGONAL HARDBOARD SIDING

◆ Use the following means to prevent gaps in the siding which permit the movement of water through the siding:

- Caulk joints at the corners and at window and door openings, except for those ventilation gaps used as part of the rain-screen wall (see Figure 29).

- For wood, use lumber that is free from splits, knot holes, and loose knots.

- To prevent future shrinkage and cracking, use siding material that has a moisture content of less than 10 percent.

◆ To help drain water away and stop the flow of water through the joints of wood and hardboard siding, take the following precautions:

- Cut the butt joints of diagonally installed siding so that the joints are vertical (see Figure 30).

- Stagger butt joints in alternate siding courses as much as possible.

- Mitre or lap siding joints at outside corners where corner boards are not used.

◆ For hardboard:

– use joint moulds and provide a 5-mm (1/4-in.) space to accommodate any expansion (see Figure 31);

– where premoulded corner and butt joint pieces are used with hardboard lap siding, follow the manufacturer's instructions for proper installation (see Figure 32);

– ensure that all joints are over framing members; and

– provide a 3-mm (1/8-in.) space at the butt joint between the siding and the window and door trim, and caulk this joint (Figure 33).

◆ For wood:

– lap horizontal bevel siding at least 25 mm (1 in.); and

– cut joints in vertical siding at a 45-degree bevel to allow the shedding of water towards the exterior.

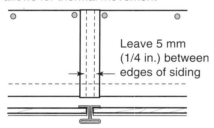

FIGURE 31
JOINT ACCESSORIES FOR HARDBOARD SIDING

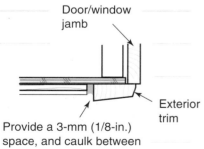

FIGURE 32
SPACE BETWEEN SIDING AND WINDOW TRIM

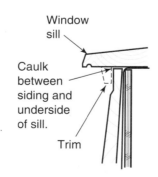

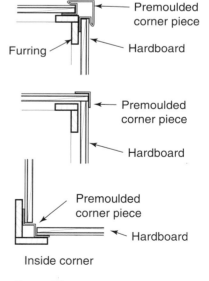

FIGURE 33
PREMOULDED CORNER PIECES FOR HARDBOARD

PROBLEM
WATER PENETRATION THROUGH SIDING

CAUSE

Poor drainage of wall elements and inadequate drips at sills or joints

SOLUTIONS

◆ Ensure that rainwater is prevented from moving inward toward the wall cavity and that positive drainage is provided.
  - Install flashing at the head of door and window frames and where two wall materials meet (see Figure 34).
  - Provide adequate outward slopes to window and door sills.

◆ Provide saw kerfs or formed chases to stop capillary action that can draw rainwater up the underside of window and door sills and into the siding.

◆ Create 3-mm (1/8-in.) gaps in the lap joints of horizontal siding. The gaps can be achieved with round-headed nails or wedges (see Figure 35).

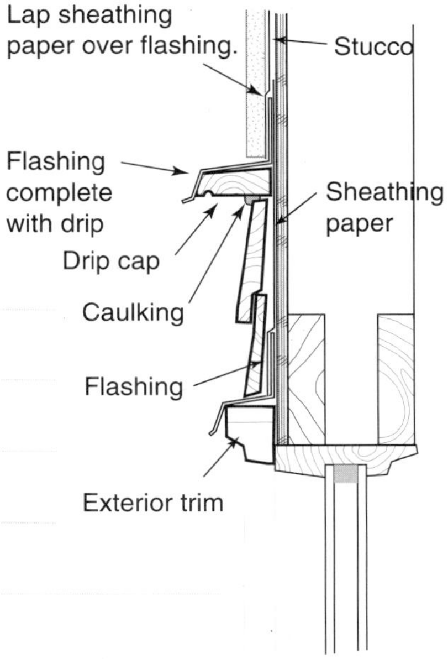

Lap sheathing
paper over flashing.
Stucco

Flashing
complete
with drip

Drip cap

Caulking

Flashing

Sheathing
paper

Exterior trim

FIGURE 34
FLASHING INSTALLATION

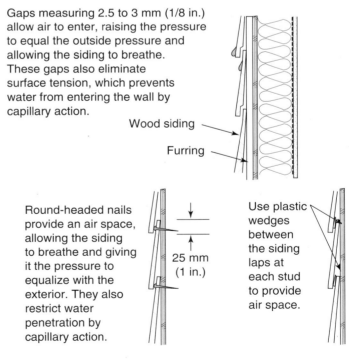

Gaps measuring 2.5 to 3 mm (1/8 in.) allow air to enter, raising the pressure to equal the outside pressure and allowing the siding to breathe. These gaps also eliminate surface tension, which prevents water from entering the wall by capillary action.

Wood siding

Furring

Round-headed nails provide an air space, allowing the siding to breathe and giving it the pressure to equalize with the exterior. They also restrict water penetration by capillary action.

25 mm
(1 in.)

Use plastic wedges between the siding laps at each stud to provide air space.

FIGURE 35
CREATING GAPS IN LAP JOINTS

PROBLEM
PREMATURE DETERIORATION

Wood siding deteriorates prematurely because of moisture-induced wood rot.

CAUSE

Condensation from air leakage and vapour diffusion on the back face of siding can lead to premature deterioration. The movement of moisture through wood siding can create external stains and mildew and cause paint to peel. Similarly, inadequate clearance of siding from grade level or roofing can result in constant saturation of the siding and lead to damage.

SOLUTIONS

Prevent the damage caused by condensation.

◆ When humid indoor air leaks through the exterior wall and condenses on the back face of wood and hardboard siding, it creates ideal conditions for the growth of fungi. Take the following precautions:

   – Install a continuous air-barrier system to minimize air leakage from the interior of the building.

   – Reduce vapour diffusion through the wall by providing a vapour barrier (polyethylene or vapour-barrier paint) on the inside surface of the exterior walls.

   – Use a single layer of 15-lb sheathing paper between the sheathing and the siding, lapped 100 mm (4 in.) around the edges.

Prevent rot by keeping siding at least 200 mm (8 in.) above grade (see Figure 36) or 50 mm (2 in.) above the abutting roof junction (see Figure 37).

◆ Water may be wicked by capillary action into wood and hardboard siding that rest on grade or are too close to grade. This water can lead to wood rot.

Prevent the presence of moisture caused by rain penetration or condensation, which warps and twists siding materials.

◆ Increase the drying potential of the siding by providing increased drainage, more air circulation on the back side (refer to rain-screen principles in section 3.1.3), and capillary breaks on the lower edges. Install siding over furring strips.

Avoid the use of inferior-grade wood siding and siding that has been damaged on the site.

◆ Use clear lumber, free of checks, cupping, splits, and knot holes. To use other than good quality lumber is a false economy.

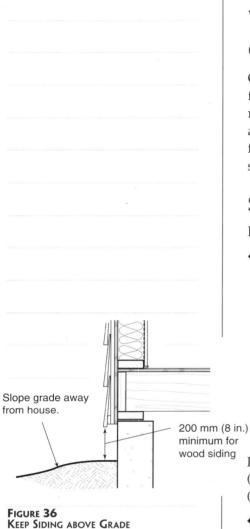

Slope grade away from house.

200 mm (8 in.) minimum for wood siding

FIGURE 36
KEEP SIDING ABOVE GRADE

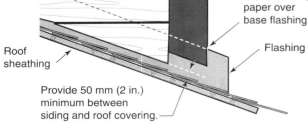

Lap sheathing paper over base flashing.

Flashing

Roof sheathing

Provide 50 mm (2 in.) minimum between siding and roof covering.

FIGURE 37
KEEP SIDING ABOVE ROOF JUNCTIONS

3.4.3 VINYL AND METAL SIDING

PROBLEM

WATER PENETRATION

Water can penetrate through the joints of vinyl and metal siding, soaking insulation, and deteriorating framing members and interior finishes.

CAUSE

Poor detailing and construction of joints between siding strips at corners and around windows and doors

SOLUTIONS

◆ Drain water away, and prevent the flow of water through the joints of vinyl and metal siding, by taking the following precautions:
  - Follow the manufacturer's instructions for installing the siding (see Figure 38).
  - With diagonal siding, cut the joints perpendicular to the ground, and overlap the lower strip with the upper strip (see Figure 39).
  - Ensure that all joints in alternate courses are staggered by at least 900 mm (36 in.).

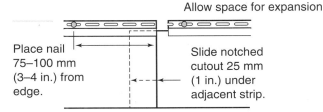

Allow space for expansion

Place nail 75–100 mm (3–4 in.) from edge.

Slide notched cutout 25 mm (1 in.) under adjacent strip.

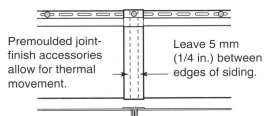

Premoulded joint-finish accessories allow for thermal movement.

Leave 5 mm (1/4 in.) between edges of siding.

FIGURE 38
JOINT DETAILS FOR METAL AND VINYL SIDING

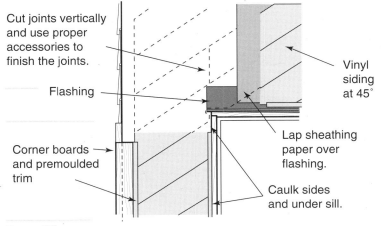

Cut joints vertically and use proper accessories to finish the joints.

Flashing

Corner boards and premoulded trim

Vinyl siding at 45°

Lap sheathing paper over flashing.

Caulk sides and under sill.

FIGURE 39
DIAGONAL VINYL SIDING

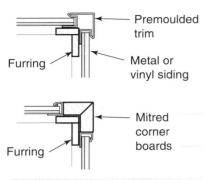

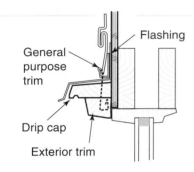

FIGURE 40
PREMOULDED CORNER DETAILS FOR
ALUMINUM, VINYL, AND WOOD SIDING

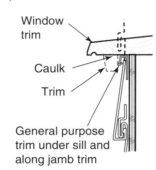

FIGURE 41
FINISH AROUND DOORS AND WINDOWS

◆ Take the following precautions to ensure that corner recesses drain water away from the interior:

– Use only premoulded corner-piece accessories on every outside corner (see Figure 40 for typical corner details suggested by manufacturers).

CAUSE

Incorrect detailing around windows and doors

SOLUTIONS

◆ Flashing is required at the head of windows and doors. Figure 41 illustrates the details at window and door heads, jambs, and under window sills.

PROBLEM
METAL AND VINYL SIDING DEFORMATION AND DISPLACEMENT

Deformed or displaced siding can result in openings through which water will penetrate.

CAUSE

Poor detailing to accommodate thermal expansion and contraction

SOLUTIONS

◆ Make sure that the method of application does not restrict thermal movement. Expansion and contraction induced by changes in temperature cause the most problems with vinyl and metal siding. To accommodate this movement, follow these practices:

– Apply the siding according to the manufacturer's instructions.

– Use the nail slots provided in the siding, and make sure that nails are set in the centre of the slots (see Figure 42). Do not nail through the material.

– Nailing should not be less than 400 to 450 mm (16 to 18 in.) o.c.

– Do not over-tighten nails (this may restrict movement as well as cause wavy siding). Allow approximately 0.7 mm (1/32 in.) between the nail head and siding (see Figure 43); siding is "hung," not nailed tightly.

– Where siding butts into a window or door frame, provide a space, as recommended by the manufacturer. Most products use "J" trim to cover this space (see Figure 44).

– To make joints less noticeable, lap them away from streets and entrances.

– For vinyl siding, provide a suitable joint between individual pieces—some vinyl siding products use lap joints, whereas others provide accessories. Follow the manufacturer's installation instructions.

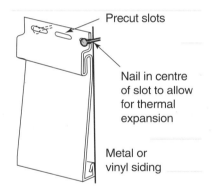

Precut slots

Nail in centre of slot to allow for thermal expansion

Metal or vinyl siding

FIGURE 42
NAIL IN CENTRE OF SLOT TO ALLOW FOR THERMAL MOVEMENT

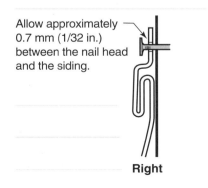

Allow approximately 0.7 mm (1/32 in.) between the nail head and the siding.

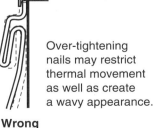

Over-tightening nails may restrict thermal movement as well as create a wavy appearance.

Right   **Wrong**

FIGURE 43
PROPER NAILING

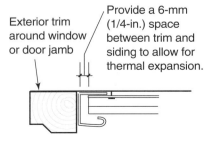

Exterior trim around window or door jamb

Provide a 6-mm (1/4-in.) space between trim and siding to allow for thermal expansion.

FIGURE 44
EXTERIOR TRIM JOINT

3.4.4 BRICK VENEER

Brick veneer can provide a durable, non-combustible and maintenance-free cladding system when properly installed.

At the same time, poor design and poor workmanship can result in defects requiring costly repairs. Problems that can occur with brick veneer installations include water penetration through the cladding to the interior wall assembly, trapped moisture in the cavity, and eventually, cracking of the cladding.

PROBLEM
WATER PENETRATION THROUGH THE VENEER

The trapping of water which passes through the veneer into the wall assembly can result in corrosion of ties and shelf-angle connectors or, if driven through the exterior sheathing, can result in deterioration of wall framing and damage to interior finishes (see also section 3.4.1, "Generic Problems").

CAUSE

Improper flashing and counterflashing installation

SOLUTIONS

◆ Minimize reliance on caulking. Provide flashing and counterflashing at all intersections between roofs and walls. This will accommodate all differential movement between the two surfaces and prevent the entry of water (see Figure 45).

◆ Install stepped flashings along the slope of the roof with a bend extending up the wall. Provide a head lap of 75 mm (3 in.) along the slope of the roof. Install counterflashing to extend 150 mm (6 in.) up the brick veneer. The flashing should be embedded a minimum of 25 mm (1 in.) into the mortar joint and lapped over the base flashing by at least 100 mm (4 in.). Make certain that the base flashing and counterflashing are the same metal to avoid deterioration caused by electrolysis.

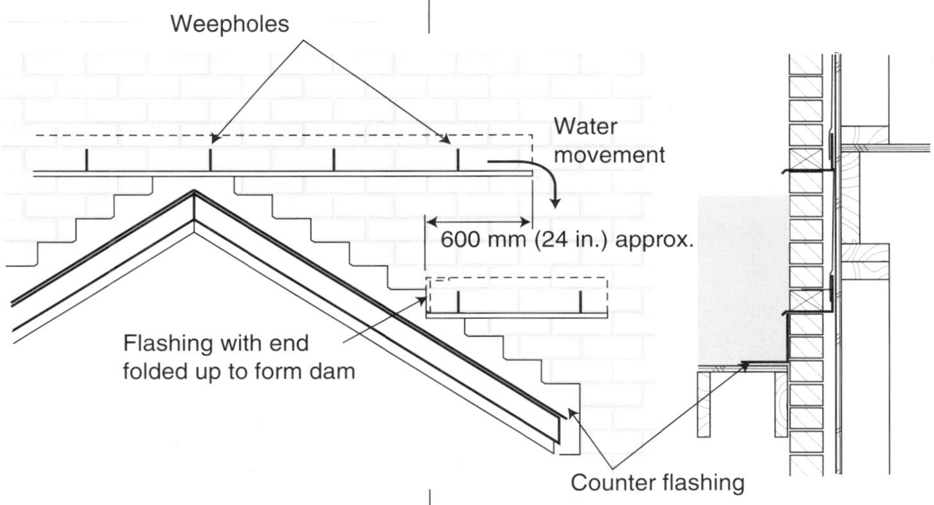

Weepholes

Water movement

600 mm (24 in.) approx.

Flashing with end folded up to form dam

Counter flashing

FIGURE 45
FLASHING OVER INTERSECTING ROOF

PROBLEM
WATER PENETRATION THROUGH THE VENEER

CAUSE

Inability of the wall system to shed water or to drain water from cavities

SOLUTIONS

◆ Ensure that water on the face of the cladding is directed away from the building. Flashings above openings should be designed to effectively shed water away from the cladding system with adequate projection and drip edges.

◆ Flashings must be installed to effectively direct water from the inside of the cavity to the outside of the cladding system. Flashings above shelf angles and base flashings must extend behind the sheathing paper on the exterior face of the sheathed frame wall. Flashing should extend continuously over the shelf angle to the exterior. The flashing should project beyond the shelf angle or brick veneer by at least 5 mm (1/4 in.) to prevent the trapping of water.

◆ Weepholes must remain clear to allow drainage of any moisture accumulating in the cavity (see Figure 46).

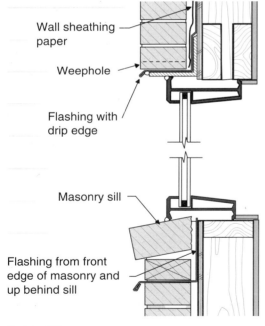

Wall sheathing paper

Weephole

Flashing with drip edge

Masonry sill

Flashing from front edge of masonry and up behind sill

FIGURE 46
FLASHING AT WINDOW

PROBLEM
CRACKING OF BRICK VENEER

Cracking of brick and mortar can provide a path for water penetration and can, in severe cases, result in a safety problem. Cracking of brick veneer often occurs where there is differential settlement in the foundation.

CAUSE

Inability of the cladding system to accommodate differential movement

SOLUTIONS

◆ Any differential movement in the foundation will be transferred through to the brick veneer, resulting in cracking (see Figure 47). Provide vertical control joints between the brick veneer and other elements of the cladding systems to allow for differential movement. Vertical movement joints should also be provided where the foundation elements change, as they might at the connection of unheated garage foundations, for example.

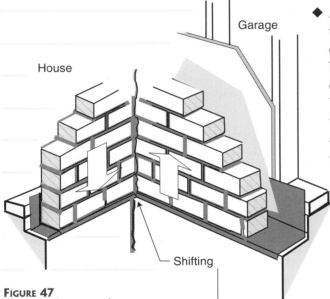

Garage

House

Shifting

FIGURE 47
VERTICAL MOVEMENT JOINT

PROBLEM
CRACKING OF BRICK VENEER

CAUSE

Installation of bricks during cold or wet weather

In cold conditions, freezing mortar with high moisture levels will expand, resulting in cracking mortar and brickwork.

SOLUTIONS

◆ Keep bricks off the ground, remove any plastic wrapping materials, and cover the bricks with a tarpaulin, allowing air circulation to remove moisture from the bricks.

◆ When mixing mortar in cold weather, reduce the quantity of mix water, and use warm water. Maintain the temperature of the mortar above 5°C (40°F). Keep sand on site covered to reduce moisture content; heat sand and ensure that there are no frozen lumps in the mix. Tent the area to be bricked, loading bricks into the heated area to raise their temperature. Cover all unfinished work to prevent water or ice from getting into the masonry wall. Tool the mortar joints only when they are stiff enough to mark a thumbprint. Raked joints are not recommended.

CAUSE

Masonry veneer can bend and crack under wind pressures where adequate lateral support is not provided.

SOLUTIONS

◆ Corrosion-resistant masonry veneer ties are required for brick veneer that is thicker than 75 mm (2-15/16 in.). Ties must be at least 1 mm (1/32 in.) thick, 22 mm (7/8 in.) wide, and shaped to provide a key with the mortar. Fasteners for ties should penetrate no less than 30 mm (1-1/4 in.) (see Figure 48).

Veneer Tie Spacing	
Maximum Vertical Spacing, mm (in.)	Maximum Horizontal Spacing, mm (in.)
400 (16)	800 (32)
500 (20)	600 (24)
600 (24)	400 (16)

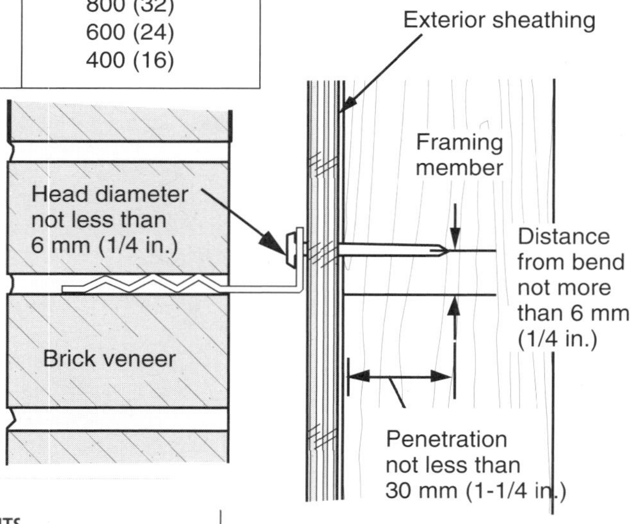

FIGURE 48
BRICK TIE REQUIREMENTS

Labels in figure: Head diameter not less than 6 mm (1/4 in.); Brick veneer; Exterior sheathing; Framing member; Distance from bend not more than 6 mm (1/4 in.); Penetration not less than 30 mm (1-1/4 in.)

3.4.5 STUCCO
INTRODUCTION

Stucco is used in many parts of Canada and provides a great deal of design flexibility, relatively high levels of envelope airtightness, and, when properly installed, can provide a durable and maintenance-free exterior finish.

At the same time, the number of stucco-related problems experienced across the country shows a poor understanding of correct design and installation practices. In virtually all parts of the country, stucco installations are prematurely failing—almost always as a result of uncontrolled moisture movement through wall systems. The trapping of moisture behind stucco—whether generated from the exterior or from the interior—can result in rapid deterioration of the finish.

As a general rule, stucco defects (see Figure 49) are the result of

- inadequate shedding of exterior rain or snow from around openings and penetrations in the stucco;

- excessive moisture-loading on the stucco, either as a function of inadequate clearances from grade or roof materials, or as a result of moisture pooling on horizontal stucco surfaces;

- penetration of rain and snow through openings in the stucco into the wall assembly; and

- trapping of moisture-laden interior house air in the wall assembly behind the stucco.

To a large extent, the problems reflect the weakness of systems designed with a face seal, where the major line of protection is subject to environmental deterioration and degradation. Without regular and effective maintenance, these systems are prone to leakage. Many designers also show a poor understanding of the need to properly drain the wall assembly in the event that moisture does accumulate behind the stucco.

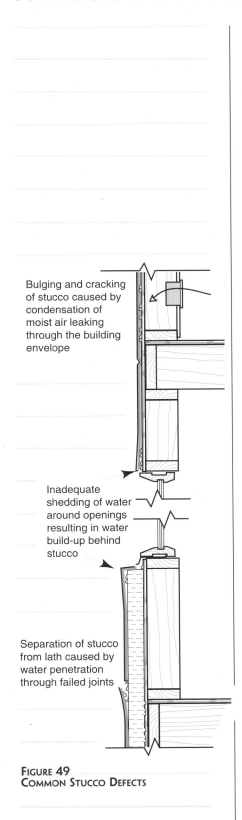

Bulging and cracking of stucco caused by condensation of moist air leaking through the building envelope

Inadequate shedding of water around openings resulting in water build-up behind stucco

Separation of stucco from lath caused by water penetration through failed joints

FIGURE 49
COMMON STUCCO DEFECTS

PROBLEM

MOISTURE DAMAGE INSIDE THE WALL ASSEMBLY

CAUSE

Entry of rainwater and snow around penetrations

Poorly flashed and sealed penetrations are the most typical sources of water leakage into the wall assembly. Where water is not adequately diverted from around windows, doors, vents, and other penetrations, it can run behind the stucco into the assembly. Sheathing-membrane failure will allow water to penetrate into the framing assembly. Water standing in the assembly can eventually lead to rotting of the structural members and sheathing, and staining of the interior finishes.

SOLUTIONS

Use approved sheathing paper or house wrap.

◆ Tar-saturated felts/papers are not permitted as sheathing membrane below stucco. Ensure that sheathing paper or house wrap provides total coverage and is free of rips and tears. Additional protection can be provided by using doubled layers of building paper or house wrap.

Install sheathing paper correctly around openings to prevent water penetration.

◆ Sheathing paper or house wrap must be installed in a shingled manner, allowing water to run down the wall. Overlap the piece of sheathing paper at the bottom of the opening with the sheathing paper that surrounds the opening (see Figure 50).

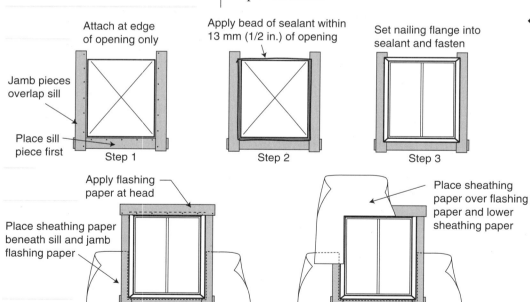

FIGURE 50
SHEATHING PAPER APPLICATION AROUND OPENINGS

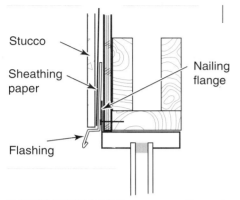

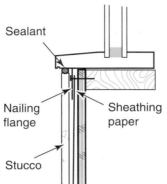

FIGURE 51
FINISH AROUND DOORS AND WINDOWS

Use proper flashing and sealing techniques around window and door penetrations (see Figure 51).

◆ Flash windows and doors to divert water from the cladding in all locations where the distance from the tops of windows or doors to the soffit is more than one quarter of the soffit overhang length.

◆ Extend head flashings up the wall a minimum of 50 mm (2 in.), ensuring that the building paper overlaps the flashing.

Use good sealing techniques around window and door penetrations.

◆ Where stucco runs up to windows and doors, install an elastomeric sealant to prevent water penetration.

◆ Where door and window sills do not provide total protection from water penetration, an elastomeric sealant should be applied below the sill.

CAUSE

Entry of rainwater and snow at the junction of different cladding materials

Missing or poorly installed flashing at the junction of different elements of the cladding system can often result in water penetrating behind the stucco, causing damage to the wall assembly.

SOLUTIONS

Install building paper and flashings correctly to ensure positive drainage.

◆ Sheathing paper must overlap any installed flashing. The flashing should extend up the wall a minimum of 50 mm (2 in.) beneath the building paper. Flashings should overlap the sheathing paper below. Do not seal the space above the flashing, as it is designed to shed any water running behind the stucco (see Figure 52).

◆ An elastomeric caulking should be used to seal the space between the stucco and underside of the flashing.

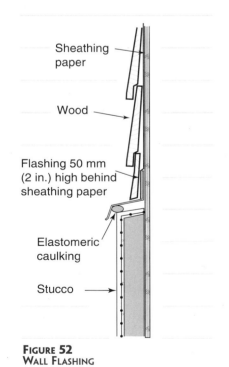

FIGURE 52
WALL FLASHING

Provide adequate clearances and flashing and counterflashing where stucco meets horizontal surfaces.

◆ Stucco should have clearance from grade of a least 200 mm (8 in.) unless applied directly over concrete or masonry.

◆ Apply flashings and counterflashings where stucco intersects with a horizontal surface, such as a flat roof (see Figure 53).

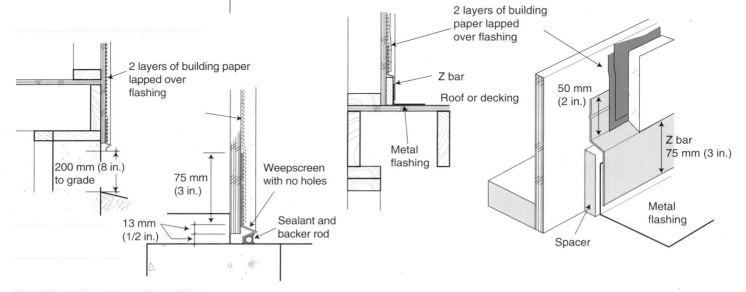

FIGURE 53
FLASHING OPTIONS

CAUSE

Entry of rainwater and snow through cracks in stucco

Like other masonry products, stucco can develop cracks due to improper curing, improper mixing, or lack of accommodation for expansion and contraction.

SOLUTIONS

Ensure that the stucco has a proper mix and is properly cured.

◆ Stucco mix requirements are specified in the NBC.

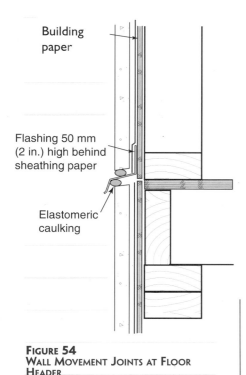

Building paper

Flashing 50 mm (2 in.) high behind sheathing paper

Elastomeric caulking

FIGURE 54
WALL MOVEMENT JOINTS AT FLOOR HEADER

◆ Water must be clean and free of contaminants and should be added at ratios identified in Table 1. The addition of too much water to the mix will weaken the stucco and can result in excessive shrinkage.

Stucco Mixes by Volume			
Portland Cement	Masonry Cement Type H	Lime	Aggregate
1 1	— 1	0.25 to 1 —	3.25 to 4 parts per part of cementitious material

Table 1
Stucco Mixes (by Volume) (NBC 9.28.5.1)

◆ The addition of plasticizers can improve workability. All admixtures must conform with CAN3-A266-2-M.

◆ Allow enough time between coats to promote good curing. Follow the manufacturer's installation recommendations.

Provide movement joints to accommodate normal shrinkage in the wall framing.

◆ Framing lumber will normally shrink as it dries after construction, most noticeably at floor header assemblies. Provide a movement joint, with appropriate flashings, above the floor header to accommodate structural movement (see Figure 54).

Properly fasten stucco lath to the framing, and reinforce it at the corners to provide additional strength.

◆ On vertical surfaces, space lath fasteners not more than 150 mm (6 in.) o.c. vertically and 400 mm (16 in.) o.c. horizontally or 100 mm (4 in.) vertically and 600 mm (24 in.) horizontally. Other fastening patterns can be used as long as there are at least 20 fasteners per square metre (two fasteners per square foot) of wall surface (see Figure 55).

◆ Reinforce metal lath at the corners of buildings and wherever the stucco is returned at window and door openings.

◆ Use a vertical strip of lath or reinforcement extending not less than 150 mm (6 in.) from either side of the corner. Alternatively, overlap lath at corners by a minimum of 150 mm (6 in.) (see Figure 56).

Fully embed the stucco lath in the stucco.

◆ Where the stucco lath is not adequately covered (embedded) after installation of the three required coats of stucco, the lath can rust. Rusting will result in expansion of the space taken up by the lath and in cracking of the exterior surface of the stucco.

◆ Metal lath should be completely covered by the first, or base coat, of stucco.

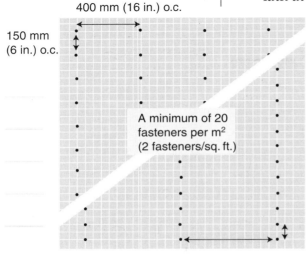

400 mm (16 in.) o.c.

150 mm (6 in.) o.c.

A minimum of 20 fasteners per m² (2 fasteners/sq. ft.)

100 mm (4 in.) o.c

600 mm (24 in.) o.c.

FIGURE 55
NAILING PATTERNS

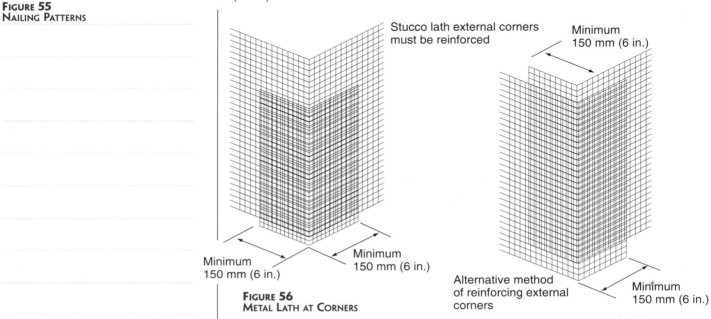

Stucco lath external corners must be reinforced

Minimum 150 mm (6 in.)

Minimum 150 mm (6 in.)

Minimum 150 mm (6 in.)

Alternative method of reinforcing external corners

Minimum 150 mm (6 in.)

FIGURE 56
METAL LATH AT CORNERS

PROBLEM

POOR AESTHETIC FINISH OF WALL

CAUSE

Poor mixing of stucco

Both the texture and colour of the finish coat of stucco can vary from batch to batch if good quality control practices are not followed.

SOLUTIONS

Ensure consistency in the batching and mixing of the finish coat materials.

◆ On-site batching of stucco requires careful attention to ensure that consistency between batches is maintained.

◆ Carefully measure quantities of materials in the mix, and follow similar mixing routines for each batch.

SECTION 3.5   DRYWALL
INTRODUCTION

Drywall (or more specifically gypsum board) is a major source of consumer complaints. In addition to having a high degree of visibility, drywall depends heavily on a number of tradespeople, especially framers.

There is now a greater frequency of problems with drywall application based on wetter framing materials, higher levels of insulation, faster construction scheduling, and an increase in construction during winter months.

3.5.1 NAIL POPS
PROBLEM
NAIL POPS

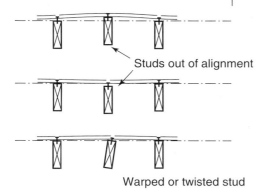

Shrinkage of wood dimension

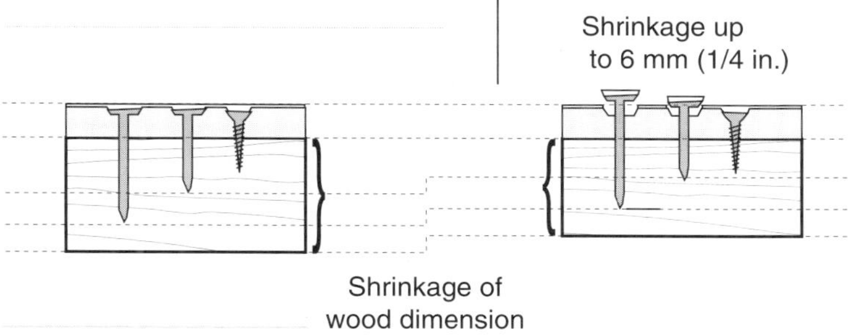

FIGURE 57
NAIL POPPING (EXAGGERATED)

CAUSE

Wet framing lumber

Shrinkage up to 6 mm (1/4 in.)

◆ As framing lumber dries, shrinkage occurs. As the studs dry and shrink relative to the fasteners, the studs pull away from the drywall. A 10 percent change in moisture content can cause a spruce or fir stud to shrink up to 6 mm (1/4 in.). Any subsequent movement of the board will cause the fastener to "pop" (see Figure 57).

Poor framing practices

SOLUTIONS

◆ Use framing lumber with the lowest possible moisture content (maximum 14 percent moisture content where possible). Avoid lumber that is grade-stamped green; for example, choose "S-DRY" over "S-GRN", or where economically viable, use kiln-dried lumber.

◆ Protect framing lumber from rain, snow, and direct sunlight.

◆ Inspect the framing before applying gypsum board. Alignment should not vary by more than 6 mm (1/4 in.). Straighten warped studs by saw-cutting and wedging (see Figure 58).

◆ Avoid protrusions from blocking (see Figure 59).

Studs out of alignment

Warped or twisted stud

FIGURE 58
NAIL POPS CAUSED BY POOR FRAMING

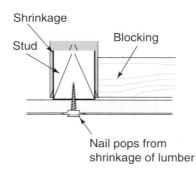

Shrinkage

Stud

Blocking

Nail pops from shrinkage of lumber

FIGURE 59
AVOIDING PROTRUSIONS

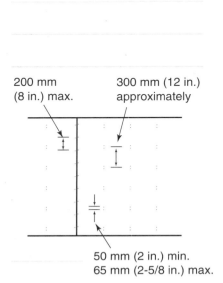

200 mm
(8 in.) max.

300 mm (12 in.)
approximately

50 mm (2 in.) min.
65 mm (2-5/8 in.) max.

FIGURE 60
DOUBLE NAILING FOR WALLS

CAUSE

Fastener pops

Some builders suggest that screws with a coarse thread have greater resistance to popping.

SOLUTIONS

◆ Apply hand or mechanical pressure when fastening to ensure that the board is making contact with the framing.

◆ Tack board in place, then return to complete nailing or screwing.

◆ Use screwing or double nailing to draw the board tighter to the stud (see Figure 60).

◆ Stagger fasteners to reduce the diagonal distances between nails or screws.

◆ If a nail or screw breaks the surface of the paper, it loses its hold on the board. Drive a second fastener close to the first.

3.5.2 CRACKING PROBLEM

OTHER TYPES OF CRACKING

CAUSE

Vibration

Exterior fastening of brick ties, siding, or trim can loosen drywall nails.

SOLUTIONS

◆ Schedule drywall installation after most exterior work has been completed.

CAUSE

Shrinkage of compound

SOLUTIONS

◆ To prevent surface cracking of the compound, do not overwater mix, and avoid rapid drying in hot weather.

◆ To prevent angle cracking, avoid using too much compound in the apex of interior angles.

CAUSE

Corner bead pulling away from framing

Differential shrinkage, especially at beams or headers, can cause cracking along the corner-bead edge (see Figure 61).

SOLUTIONS

◆ Nail corner bead at 100 mm (4 in.) rather than at the usually recommended 150 mm (6 in.). Crimping alone is not sufficient.

◆ Don't extend the corner bead to the subfloor. Leave a 13-mm (1/2-in.) gap.

◆ Avoid flattening the corner bead when fastening. Ensure a sufficiently high bead for adequate cover with finishing compound.

◆ In highly visible areas, such as the opening between living and dining rooms, some builders omit corner bead and install wood trim.

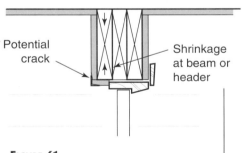

Potential crack

Shrinkage at beam or header

FIGURE 61
CORNER-BEAD CRACKING

Cause

Stresses at openings

Differential movement around openings (windows and doors) can result in stresses on the wallboard, resulting in cracking.

Solutions

◆ Avoid locating joints at the edge of the header (see Figure 62).

◆ Apply 150- to 200-mm (6- to 8-in.) lengths of joint tape diagonally to reinforce corners.

◆ Provide adequate framing to absorb vibration from door and window operation. Cut jack studs accurately.

◆ With metal framing, reinforce header and jamb intersections, or provide additional framing. Grout frames for heavy or oversized doors.

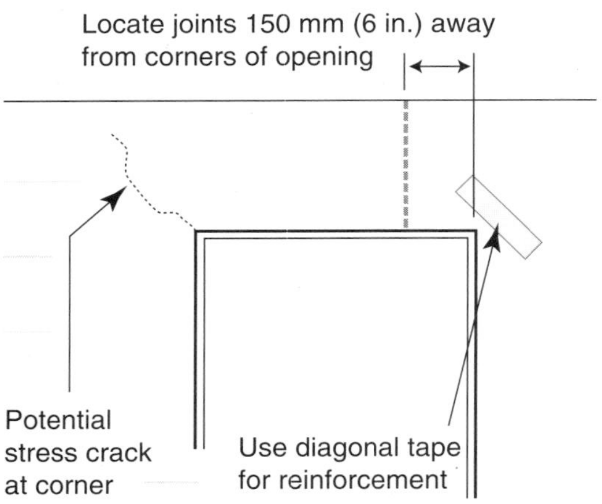

Locate joints 150 mm (6 in.) away from corners of opening

Potential stress crack at corner

Use diagonal tape for reinforcement

FIGURE 62
PREVENTING STRESS CRACKS

Cause

Inadequate corner support

Solutions

◆ Movement of drywall can cause cracking at exterior corners or where interior partitions intersect at exterior walls. Metal corner-beading can provide additional support. Nails and screws should be spaced no more than 200 mm (8 in.) at corners. Provide adequate nailing surfaces, or use drywall clips (see Figure 63).

◆ With metal studs, run drywall from the interior of the corners through to the outside face, and provide corner reinforcement (see Figure 64).

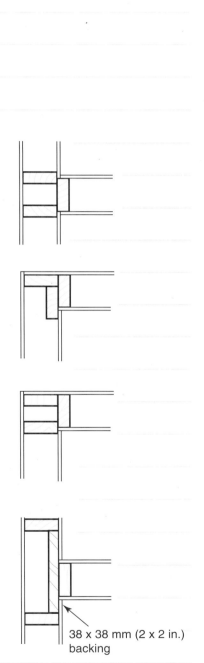

38 x 38 mm (2 x 2 in.) backing

Figure 63
Four Alternatives for Framing Interior Corners

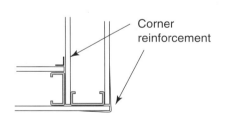
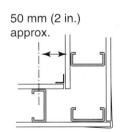

Corner reinforcement

50 mm (2 in.) approx.

Figure 64
Interior Corners with Metal Studs

PROBLEM
VISIBLE JOINTS, RIDGING, AND TAPE DELAMINATION OF DRYWALL

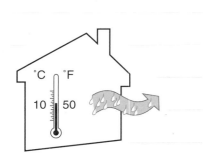

FIGURE 65
HEAT AND VENTILATION REQUIREMENTS

CAUSE

Environmental conditions

Lack of sufficient heat or ventilation, especially during winter construction

SOLUTIONS

◆ Maintain a minimum temperature of 10°C (50°F) for two days before, and four days after, treatment. Loss of bond will occur if the temperature is too cold (see Figure 65).

◆ Make sure the board is kept dry and is free of frost.

◆ Protect ready-mixed compounds from freezing.

◆ Make sure there is adequate ventilation for drying. Temporary heating may cause high humidity levels.

◆ Curing of the basement slab also releases moisture into the air. Allow the slab to cure, and remove any surface water before finishing the drywall, or delay pouring the slab until primer paint has been applied to the drywall. Provide ventilation.

CAUSE

Damaged board edges

SOLUTIONS

◆ Schedule board delivery before installing windows, or leave key windows out for ease of delivery.

◆ Avoid carrying the boards great distances or up tight stairways. Consult with the supplier on delivery preferences.

◆ Stack boards neatly in the centre of the rooms to protect board corners. Damaged ends are susceptible to ridging.

◆ Avoid temporary storage outside. Protect the boards from rain, wet snow, and dampness.

3.5.3 JOINTS
PROBLEM
VISIBLE JOINTS, RIDGING, AND TAPE DELAMINATION

CAUSE

Improper application of joint tape and compounds

SOLUTIONS

◆ Make sure that joint tape is completely embedded in the compound to prevent bubbling.

◆ Avoid overwatering the mix or using heavy fills.

◆ Follow the manufacturer's directions and NBC requirements.

◆ Allow joint compounds to dry completely between coats.

◆ Paint only after compounds have fully dried to prevent joint darkening.

◆ Feather butt joints wider than edge joints (see Figure 66).

◆ Avoid oversanding the compound or sanding the board itself. This can result in "flashing"—different gloss textures on the joint and board.

◆ In extremely bright areas, even minor surface flaws will be readily apparent. Consider using a flat, or low-sheen, paint to minimize apparent defects.

CAUSE

Lumber shrinkage

Shrinkage at headers may cause ridging, especially at stairways (see Figure 67). Ridging can also occur when studs and joists warp and twist.

SOLUTIONS

◆ Float board across headers, fastening above and below, but not directly to the header itself. Alternatively, use horizontal control joints, and conceal them with trim.

◆ Inspect framing before installing the drywall. Straighten or replace warped studs. Use kiln-dried lumber, if possible.

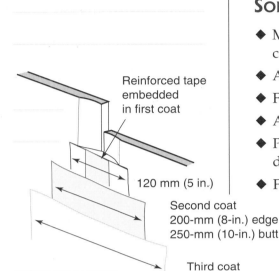

Reinforced tape embedded in first coat

120 mm (5 in.)

Second coat
200-mm (8-in.) edge
250-mm (10-in.) butt

Third coat
250-mm (10-in.) edge
400-mm (16-in.) butt

FIGURE 66
TYPICAL JOINT TREATMENT

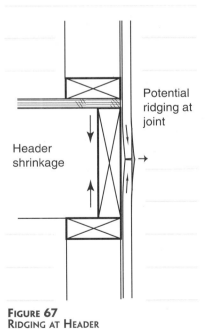

Potential ridging at joint

Header shrinkage

FIGURE 67
RIDGING AT HEADER

Cause

Improper board application

Solutions

◆ Fasten boards from the centre outward to avoid putting them into compression. Don't force oversized panels into place.

◆ Minimize butt joints by using the longest sheets possible.

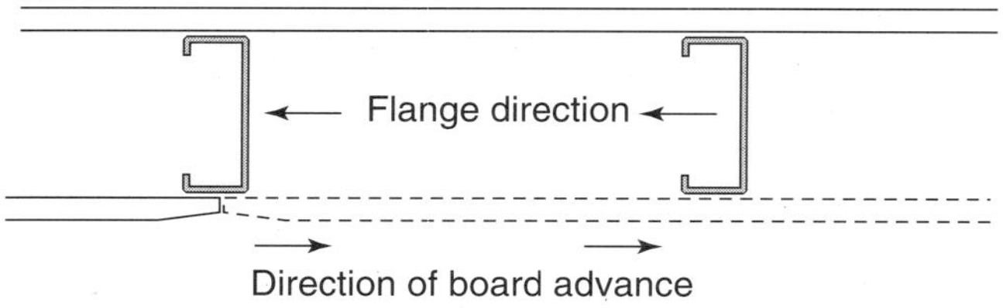

◆ Install metal studs with all flanges facing the same direction, and mount drywall in the direction opposite to flanges (see Figure 68). This prevents flange deflection and joint problems.

←— Flange direction ←—

Direction of board advance

FIGURE 68
MOUNTING DIRECTION

3.5.4 MOISTURE PROBLEM

DETERIORATION IN HIGH-MOISTURE AREAS

CAUSE

Excessive humidity and dampness in bathrooms, laundry areas, and exterior soffits

Moisture absorption can cause expansion and powdering of the gypsum core, delamination of the paper face, and mold growth.

SOLUTIONS

◆ Use water-resistant gypsum board in damp areas. The NBC now requires "moisture-resistant backing" for ceramic and plastic tile on walls around bathtubs and showers.

◆ Allow a 7-mm (1/4-in.) space between the drywall and the surfaces of the tub, shower floor, or return (see Figure 69).

◆ To prevent problems at the bathtub, some builders use a cement-based board instead of gypsum board as an underlay for ceramic tile, or they install a fibreglass tub enclosure.

◆ Locate tub enclosures on interior walls.

◆ Some builders strap bathroom walls to allow an air space for improved drying.

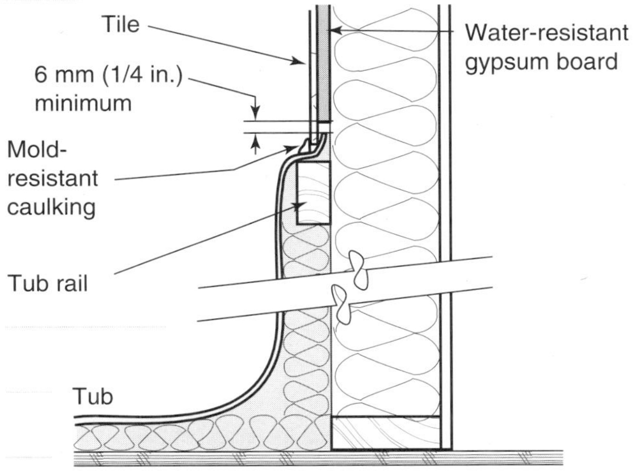

Tile

6 mm (1/4 in.) minimum

Mold-resistant caulking

Tub rail

Tub

Water-resistant gypsum board

FIGURE 69
BATHTUB DETAIL

Section 3.6 Additional Reading

Source	Publication
Canadian Gypsum Company Ltd. P.O. Box 4034 Terminal A 777 Bay Street Toronto ON M5W 1K8 905 803-5600	*Drywall Construction Handbook,* 1990
Canadian Home Builders' Association 150 Laurier Avenue West, Suite 500 Ottawa ON K1P 5J4 613 230-3060	*CHBA Builders' Manual,* 1994
Canada Mortgage and Housing Corporation Canadian Housing Information Centre 700 Montreal Road Ottawa ON K1A 0P7 613 748-2367	*Canadian Wood-Frame House Construction,* 1997 NHA 5031
Ontario New Home Warranty Program 5160 Yonge Street, 6th Floor North York ON M2N 6L9 416 229-9200	*The Details of Air Barrier Systems,* 1994 *Code and Construction Guide for Housing,* 1993 *Building Smart: Truss Uplift,* 1993

CHAPTER 4

Introduction

ROOF AND CEILING SYSTEMS

This chapter presents the most common roof and ceiling system problems and shows Canadian home builders how to avoid them. It does this by improving your understanding of design principles, material performance expectations, and proper construction procedures.

Three main categories are presented: roofing materials, the roof structure, and the interior finish are discussed as they relate to structural deterioration and damage or to water leakage.

The roof constitutes the weather barrier for the attic and the remainder of the house, so it is important that it be durable. Recurring problems with such established roofing materials as asphalt shingles and wood shingles and shakes reflect the need for improved procedures. Tile and metal roofs, which are gaining popularity, require extra care when they are designed, scheduled, and installed.

Of course, good roofing structure is critical. Without a solid structure, sagging, shifting, and water leakage are likely. Proper design and good workmanship provide a good base for the roofing materials, which in turn offer protection to the structural elements of the roof.

Problems with the interior ceiling finish, including sagging, wetting, and the formation of mold, are also addressed. These problems can usually be traced to structural deficiencies or to problems with the roofing materials. Proper construction scheduling and control of the interior environment of the building during construction are also covered.

This chapter does not present all aspects of roof construction, and some of the problems discussed here are more prevalent in certain parts of the country than in others, influenced either by regional construction techniques or local weather conditions. However, this chapter provides most of the information you will need to identify the causes of problems so that you may avoid creating imperfections during construction.

Section 4.1 Roofing Materials
INTRODUCTION

Roofing materials are designed to protect the home from the elements. These materials include shingles, shakes, metal roofing, sheathing paper, and flashings. The failure of any of the materials, or poor installation practices, can result in premature deterioration and leakage.

This section deals with water leakage that is caused by improper installation and by structural problems. It also covers premature deterioration of roofing materials due to interior conditions or due to the elements.

Various types of roofing materials are discussed in this section, including asphalt shingles, wood shingles, wood shakes, metal roofing, concrete tiles, and clay tiles. The flashings are equally important, as they work with the roofing materials to make a tight membrane. Step flashings, valley flashings, cricket roofs, and vent flashings are all addressed.

Ice damming and eave protection are also covered in this section, as are the requirements for proper installation of attic and ceiling insulation and ventilation.

4.1.1 STRUCTURAL DETERIORATION AND DAMAGE
PROBLEM
BROKEN ASPHALT SHINGLES

CAUSE

Winds can lift shingle tabs, causing them to break.

Strong winds can lift shingle tabs, especially during hot periods in summer when the adhesive sealant is not as resistant to lifting. Degradation occurs as the wind bends the shingle tabs back and forth, eventually resulting in breakage.

SOLUTIONS

Tab all shingles, including those that are self-sealing.

◆ Follow the manufacturer's directions for the best temperature range for installing self-sealing shingles. Asphalt shingles are most workable in temperature ranges of 10° to 23°C (50° to 74°F). Below 10°C (50°F), asphalt shingles become stiff, and the self-sealant does not adhere properly. Self-sealing shingles may require a few weeks of warm weather to seal properly (see Figure 1).

◆ If the shingles are applied in cold weather, seal them manually when temperatures rise above 10°C (50°F). Apply a 25-mm (1-in.) spot of adhesive sealant or roofing cement under the centre of each tab. Apply extra roofing cement to the tabs at gables.

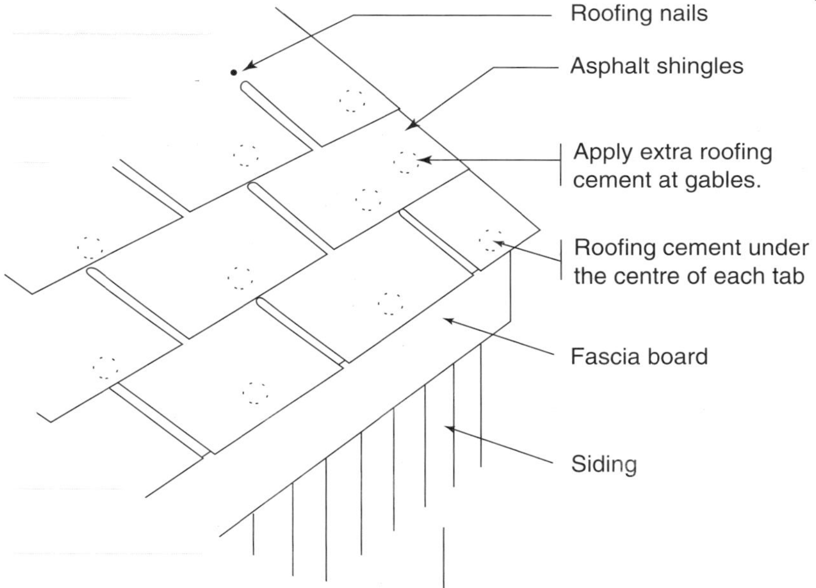

Roofing nails

Asphalt shingles

Apply extra roofing cement at gables.

Roofing cement under the centre of each tab

Fascia board

Siding

FIGURE 1
TABBING SHINGLES

PROBLEM
CURLED ASPHALT SHINGLES

CAUSE

Water vapour penetration

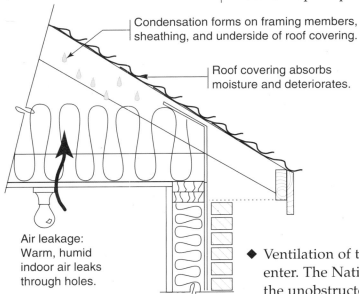

Condensation forms on framing members, sheathing, and underside of roof covering.

Roof covering absorbs moisture and deteriorates.

Air leakage: Warm, humid indoor air leaks through holes.

FIGURE 2
ROOFING DETERIORATION FROM MOISTURE

When water migrates to the underside of asphalt shingles, the shingles can curl, cup, or shrink (see Figure 2).

SOLUTIONS

Reduce the amount of moisture accumulating on the underside of the shingles.

◆ The amount of water vapour that enters the attic space can be minimized by proper installation of air and vapour barriers. Minimize all paths of potential air leakage into the attic.

◆ Ventilation of the roof space allows moist air to exit and dry air to enter. The National Building Code of Canada (NBC) requires that the unobstructed vent area be not less than 1/300 of the insulated ceiling area. For roof slopes of less than 1 in 6, the unobstructed vent area shall be not less than 1/150 of the insulated ceiling area.

◆ Ventilation should be uniformly distributed, with at least 25 percent at the top and at least 25 percent at the bottom.

◆ Apply roofing only on dry roof sheathing and decking.

◆ Ensure that soffit vents are not obstructed by insulation.

PROBLEM

DETERIORATION OF ASPHALT SHINGLE SURFACE

CAUSE

Sunlight and high roof temperatures can cause differential hardening of the asphalt material through the shingle.

The exterior surface hardens faster than the interior. This can lead to the eventual break-up of the roofing material and the penetration of water.

SOLUTIONS

Keep roof temperatures down.

◆ Ventilate the roof space in accordance with NBC 9.19.1.2 to reduce high temperatures in attic areas (see Figure 3).

◆ Ease the effects of solar radiation by selecting lighter aggregate colours to reflect some of the radiation.

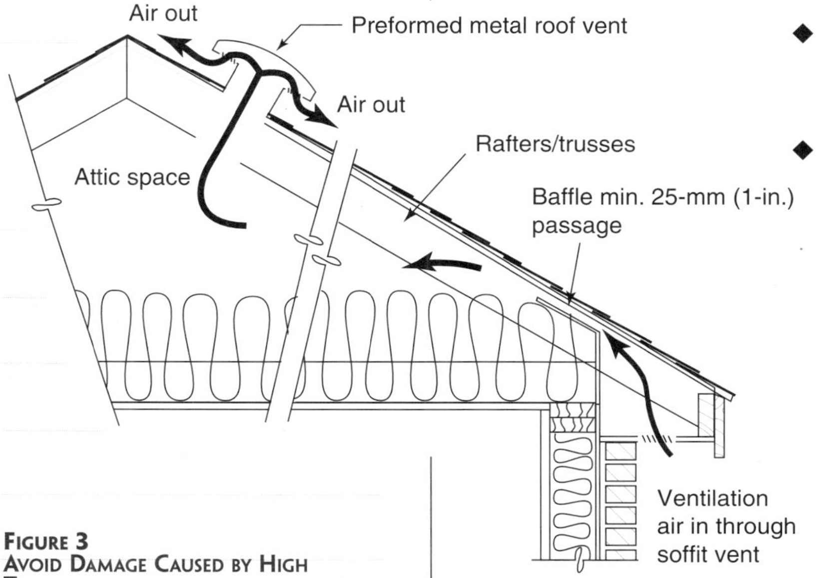

FIGURE 3
AVOID DAMAGE CAUSED BY HIGH TEMPERATURES

Air out
Preformed metal roof vent
Air out
Rafters/trusses
Attic space
Baffle min. 25-mm (1-in.) passage
Ventilation air in through soffit vent

PROBLEM

SHINGLE DEFORMATION AND DISPLACEMENT

CAUSE

Improper or inadequate roof deck or improper fastening of shingles

Many different factors can deform or displace asphalt shingles. Lumber-deck movement, incorrect sheathing thickness, spacing or installation, nail pops in the sheathing, and incorrect shingle fastening can all be factors. Persistent deformation of the decking/sheathing will weaken the roof and provide openings in the shingles through which water can penetrate.

SOLUTIONS

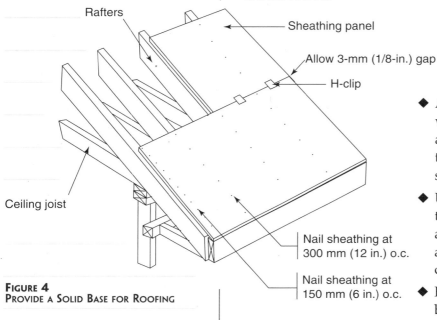

Rafters

Sheathing panel

Allow 3-mm (1/8-in.) gap

H-clip

Ceiling joist

Nail sheathing at 300 mm (12 in.) o.c.

Nail sheathing at 150 mm (6 in.) o.c.

FIGURE 4
PROVIDE A SOLID BASE FOR ROOFING

Provide a proper base on which to apply the shingles and ensure that the shingles are properly fastened (see Figure 4).

◆ Avoid lumber-deck movement associated with wet lumber. When asphalt shingles are installed over a green-lumber base, they often buckle as the wood dries and shrinks.

◆ Use dry lumber or let the lumber dry to 19 percent moisture content before applying asphalt shingles. Ventilate attic spaces to reduce humidity that can cause the decking to swell and expand.

◆ Reduce the problem of deck movement by using sheathing panels instead of board lumber for the roof deck.

◆ High wind loads will make the roof deck vibrate if the deck material is too thin or insufficiently rigid. Such vibration can loosen the shingle fastening. The required thickness of sheathing is a function of the span from rafter to rafter. The NBC requires plywood and O-2 grade waferboard and strandboard to be a minimum of 7 mm (5/16 in.) thick when supports are spaced 400 mm (16 in.) o.c. and the edges are supported. The thickness required for supports at 600 mm (24 in.) o.c. is 9 mm (3/8 in.).

◆ If green lumber is used to sheathe the roof, shrinkage of the lumber may cause nails to pop. This can damage the waterproof characteristics of the asphalt shingle roof.

◆ The two most important characteristics of shingle nails are the head size and the nails' rust resistance. Nails must be long enough to penetrate at least 12 mm (1/2 in.) into the roof sheathing. The head diameter should not be less than 9 mm (3/8 in.), and the shank should be no less than 3 mm (1/8 in.). Staples used with asphalt shingles are not to be less than 19 mm (3/4 in.) long, not less than 2 mm (1/16 in.) in diameter or thickness, and have a crown no smaller than 25 mm (1 in.).

◆ The NBC requires that shingles be fastened with no fewer than four nails or staples for a 1-m (40-in.)-wide shingle. The number of fasteners may be reduced for narrower shingles in proportion to the width of the shingles. Place fasteners between 25 mm (1 in.) and 40 mm (1-1/2 in.) from each end, with the other fasteners spaced equally between. Inadequate shingle fastening can result in displaced shingles and openings for water to penetrate. Always refer to roofing manufacturers' installation instructions (see Figure 5).

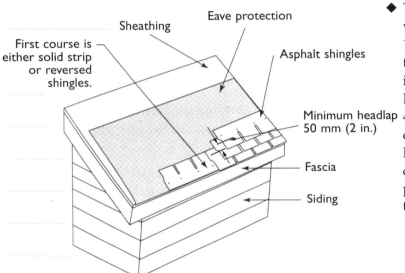

FIGURE 5
PROPER ROOFING INSTALLATION

Labels in figure:
First course is either solid strip or reversed shingles.
Sheathing
Eave protection
Asphalt shingles
Minimum headlap 50 mm (2 in.)
Fascia
Siding

PROBLEM
ROTTING OF WOOD ROOFING; RUSTING OF METAL ROOFING

CAUSE

Condensation on the underside of the roofing

When water vapour migrates to the underside of wood shingles and shakes and then condenses, the moisture can cause decay.

Condensation can form on the underside of sheet metal when warm moist air leaks or diffuses from the interior and comes in contact with roofing at a temperature that is lower than the dew point. Condensation can also form on the underside of sheet metal as a result of rapid heat transfer by conduction and radiation. This condensation will cause the metal to corrode and rust.

SOLUTIONS

Reduce the amount of moisture entering the roof cavity by installing a good air and vapour barrier. Ventilation of the attic space will lower moisture levels (see Figure 6).

◆ Install good air and vapour barriers in the house. This is especially important in the ceilings, because a positive pressure near the ceiling will force warm, moist air into the attic.

◆ Ensure all penetrations through the air barrier are properly sealed.

◆ Ventilate the attic according to the NBC. This will help control moisture that enters the attic.

◆ Use pressure-treated shingles and shakes to achieve better service life.

◆ Prevent contact with the attic conditions by installing foil or felt underlay directly under metal roofing. Avoid thermal bridges through fasteners, as they provide a good surface for condensation.

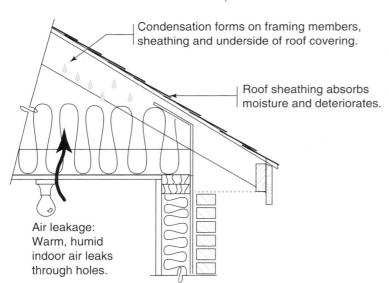

Condensation forms on framing members, sheathing and underside of roof covering.

Roof sheathing absorbs moisture and deteriorates.

Air leakage: Warm, humid indoor air leaks through holes.

FIGURE 6
MOISTURE DAMAGE TO WOOD AND METAL ROOFING

PROBLEM
CRACKED CONCRETE OR CLAY ROOF TILES

CAUSE

Damage by workers during construction

Workers who must complete exterior work in areas above roofing tiles must walk on the tiles, which may cause them to crack.

SOLUTIONS

Leave the last rows of tiles unfinished.

◆ Leave the last few rows of roof tiles unfinished until after all workers have completed exterior finishes, such as siding, stucco, painting, brickwork, etc. (see Figure 7).

◆ Install flashings and finish roof tiles when all exterior work located above the roof tiles has been completed.

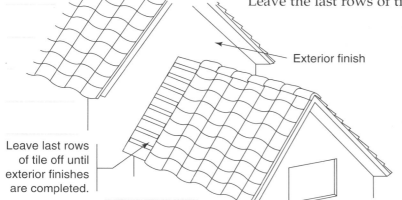

Exterior finish

Leave last rows of tile off until exterior finishes are completed.

FIGURE 7
CONCRETE OR CLAY TILE ROOF

4.1.2 WATER LEAKAGE PROBLEM

FLASHING FAILURES

CAUSE

Inadequate size and improper installation of flashings

Roof flashings are pieces of sheet metal used to prevent water or wind-driven rain through joints between materials. They are installed at wall and roof intersections, in roof valleys, and around roof penetrations. Most of the problems occur when the flashings are too small or are not installed with adequate lap and in the right locations relative to other materials.

SOLUTIONS

Flashings must have minimum sizes and must be installed properly to seal the joints between materials (see Figure 8).

◆ Attach a base flashing to the roof at the intersection of the walls and the roof, and bend it 90 degrees up the wall. If you use a stepped flashing, you must apply a head lap of 75 mm (3 in.) along the slope.

◆ Counterflashing must extend 150 mm (6 in.) up the side of the wall. When the wall finish is masonry, embed the counterflashing at least 25 mm (1 in.) into the mortar joint, and lap it over the base flashing by at least 100 mm (4 in.).

◆ For other wall finishes, counterflashing is not used, so the sheathing paper and finish material should lap over the base flashing. For wood siding, leave a 50-mm (2-in.) gap between the siding and the roof to prevent water suction into the wood.

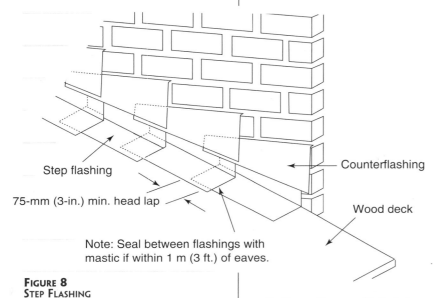

Step flashing

75-mm (3-in.) min. head lap

Counterflashing

Wood deck

Note: Seal between flashings with mastic if within 1 m (3 ft.) of eaves.

FIGURE 8
STEP FLASHING

◆ Open valleys can be flashed with sheet metal at least 600 mm (24 in.) wide or with two layers of roll roofing. If you use roll roofing, centre one layer of Type S or Type M in the valley with the mineral surface down; it should be not less than 457 mm (18 in.) wide. Provide a second layer of Type M with the mineral surface up; it should measure not less than 914 mm (36 in.) wide. Do not walk on the roll roofing valley, as the fabric may shrink, making it easy to puncture. Some areas may permit the use of felt in the valley rather than sheet metal or roll roofing (see Figures 9 and 10).

Trim roof coverings back from 12 mm (1/2 in.) to 75 mm (3 in.) from the centre line of the valley. Minimum trim at the peak and maximum at the eaves

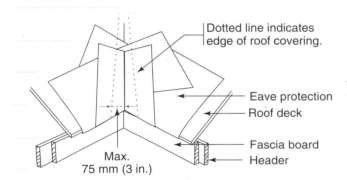

FIGURE 9
PROPER ROOFING INSTALLATION AT VALLEY

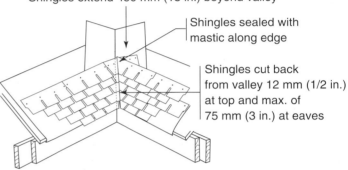

Simplified Closed Valley
Application for Asphalt Shingles

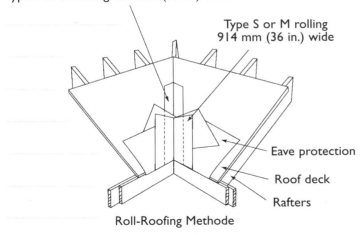

Roll-Roofing Methode

Sheet-Metal Method

FIGURE 10
VALLEY FLASHINGS

◆ Trim the roof coverings in a straight line on both sides of the valley. The distance between the finish and the centre of the valley should be no less than 50 mm (2 in.).

◆ Roof vents, plumbing vents, and metal chimneys generally come with preformed flashing. Follow the manufacturers' installation instructions to ensure watertightness.

◆ Where the upper side of a chimney on a sloping roof is more than 750 mm (30 in.) wide, protect the intersection between the roof and the chimney with sheet-metal flashing that extends up the chimney to a height equal to and not less than one sixth the width of the chimney, and not less than 150 mm (6 in.). It must extend up the roof slope to a point equal in height to the flashing on the chimney, but not less than one and a half times the shingle exposure. If you do not do this, you must install a chimney saddle (see Figure 11).

◆ Cover chimney saddles with sheet metal or roofing material of weight and quality equivalent to the roofing, and suitably flash them where they intersect with the roof. Flush and counterflush the intersection of the chimney and the saddle.

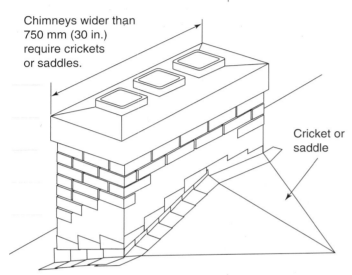

Chimneys wider than 750 mm (30 in.) require crickets or saddles.

Cricket or saddle

FIGURE 11
CRICKET ROOF AT MASONRY CHIMNEY

PROBLEM

WATER PENETRATION FROM ICE DAMMING

CAUSE

Inadequate eave protection

Ice damming is the build-up of ice at the edge of the roof, caused by heat escaping from the house and melting snow that accumulates on the roof. This water flows down under the snow covering the roof. As it reaches the outer edge of the eave over the cooler soffit area, it freezes, creating an ice dam. The ice dam stops the melt water from reaching the eave. Ice then builds up in the form of icicles and slabs, and the melt water can back up through the shingles and leak into the attic if adequate eave protection is not used.

SOLUTIONS

Adequate levels of insulation over the exterior wall in combination with ventilation between the insulation and the roof sheathing will prevent ice damming. Eave protection can also help prevent damage (see Figure 12).

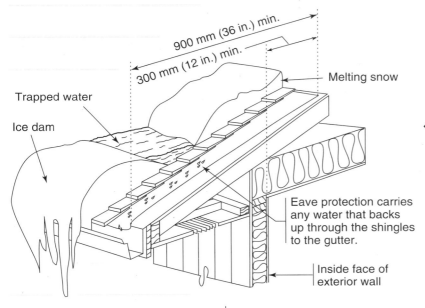

900 mm (36 in.) min.

300 mm (12 in.) min.

Melting snow

Trapped water

Ice dam

Eave protection carries any water that backs up through the shingles to the gutter.

Inside face of exterior wall

FIGURE 12
ICE DAMMING

◆ Protection at eaves and in valley intersections will stop water from penetrating through to the roof deck. Accepted eave protection options include

 – No. 15 asphalt-saturated felt laid in two plies lapped 480 mm (19 in.) and cemented together;

 – Type M or S roll roofing laid with not less than 100-mm (4-in.) head- and end-laps cemented together with lap cement;

 – glass fibre- or polyester fibre-coated base sheets;

 – self-sealing composite membranes consisting of modified bituminous coated material; or

 – ice and water shield products.

◆ Install eave protection on shingle, shake, or tile roofs, and extend it from the edge of the roof a minimum of 900 mm (36 in.) up the roof slope to a line not less than 300 mm (12 in.) inside the inner face of the exterior wall.

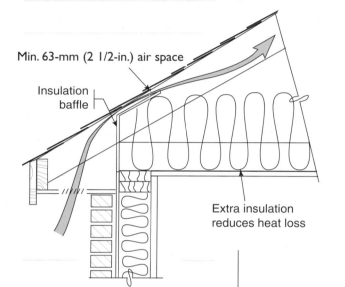

Min. 63-mm (2 1/2-in.) air space

Insulation baffle

Extra insulation reduces heat loss

FIGURE 13
INSULATION AND VENTILATION TO KEEP ROOF COOLER

◆ Low-voltage heat cables can be used in valleys to help keep the valleys clear of ice and snow.

◆ The use of high heel trusses will allow for extra insulation over the exterior wall. This will reduce the amount of heat loss from the house to the attic, decreasing the melting of snow on the roof.

◆ The use of prefabricated baffles will allow for air flow between the ceiling insulation and the underside of the roof sheathing.
This will keep the roof surface cooler and help reduce the amount of melting (see Figure 13).

PROBLEM

WATER LEAKAGE THROUGH WOOD ROOFING

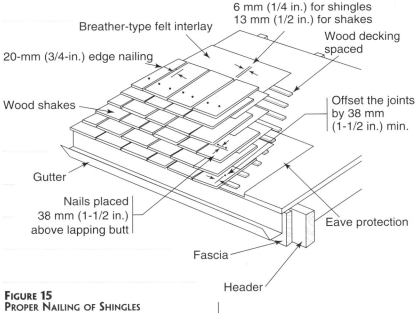

Exposure

Wood shingles

Spaced wood decking

Wood deck spacing is equal to exposure.

Rafter/truss

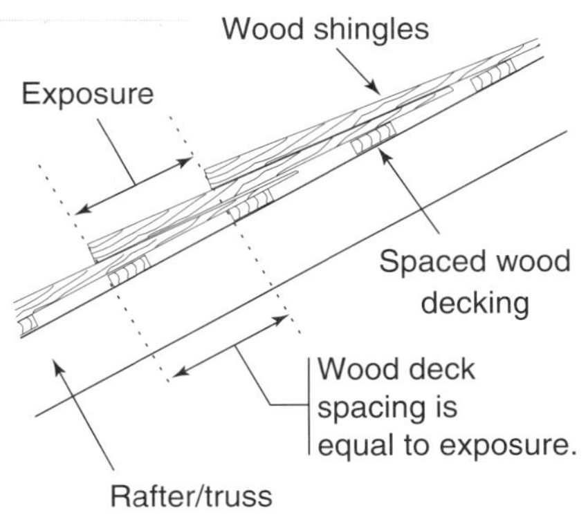

FIGURE 14
SHINGLE EXPOSURE

CAUSE

Excessive exposure length, no interlay between shake courses, and improper joint locations

SOLUTIONS

Install wood shingles and shakes according to NBC requirements.

◆ Prevent the movement of wind-driven rain through the shingled roof to the attic or roof cavity by overlapping the shingles or shakes correctly. The NBC requires that the exposure of wood shakes to wind, rain, or sun shall not exceed 190 mm (7-1/2 in.) for shakes not less than 450 mm (18 in.) long; and 250 mm (10 in.) for shakes not less than 600 mm (24 in.) long. Correct exposure for wood shingles is a function of shingle length, grade, and roof slope. No. 1 grade shingles that are 400 mm (16 in.) long can have a maximum exposure of 125 mm (5 in.); those 450 mm (18 in.) long can have a maximum exposure of 140 mm (5-1/2 in.); and those 600 mm (24 in.) long can have a maximum exposure of 190 mm (7-1/2 in.) (see Figure 14).

◆ Apply a strip of breather-type roof felt (min. 450 mm [18 in.] wide) over the top portion of the shakes, and rest it on the roof sheathing. Place the bottom end of the felt a distance two times the weather exposure above the butt. This felt interlay acts as a baffle and prevents wind-driven rain or snow from penetrating the roof cavity.

◆ Space shingles 6 mm (1/4 in.) apart, and offset them at the joints in adjacent courses by not less than 40 mm (1-1/2 in.) so that joints in alternate courses are staggered. Shakes shall be spaced 6 mm (1/4 in.) to 9 mm (3/8 in.) apart and offset at the joints in adjacent courses by not less than 40 mm (1-1/2 in.), so that joints in alternate courses are staggered (see Figure 15).

6 mm (1/4 in.) for shingles
13 mm (1/2 in.) for shakes

Breather-type felt interlay

Wood decking spaced

20-mm (3/4-in.) edge nailing

Wood shakes

Offset the joints by 38 mm (1-1/2 in.) min.

Gutter

Nails placed 38 mm (1-1/2 in.) above lapping butt

Eave protection

Fascia

Header

FIGURE 15
PROPER NAILING OF SHINGLES

PROBLEM

WATER LEAKAGE OF METAL ROOFING

CAUSE

Thermal movement

Metal has a high co-efficient of expansion. As metal expands, it can increase the size of the perforation in the metal. When it contracts, the exposed fastenings may loosen.

SOLUTIONS

Use proper anchoring systems.

◆ The best way to control thermal movement is a concealed anchor-clip system without perforations, such as sliding-hook clips or bar clips. This system securely fastens the sheet metal to the deck or structure while accommodating thermal movement (see Figure 16).

◆ Avoid using exposed bolts or screws through the metal. Thermal movement of sheet metal cannot be prevented. Use special fastenings which allow the sheet metal to move freely as it expands and contracts.

◆ Properly install neoprene seals under fasteners.

◆ Ensure fasteners are installed straight.

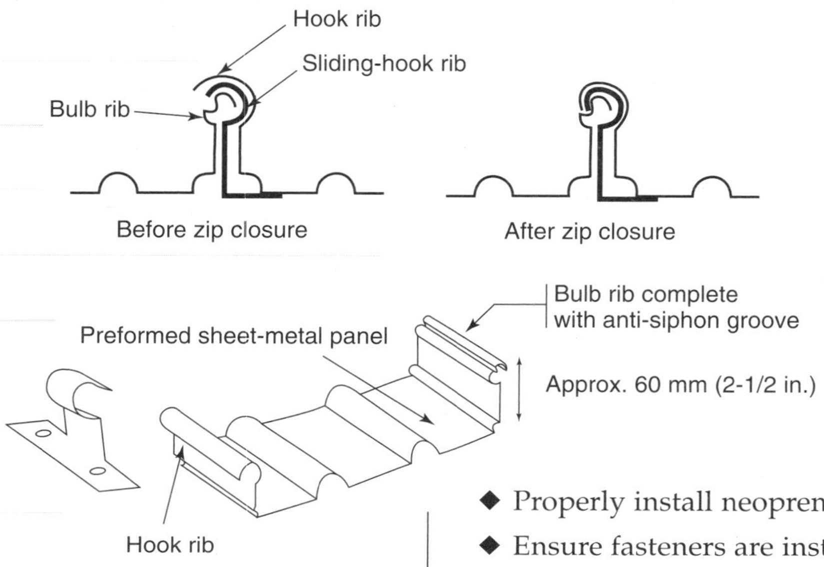

Before zip closure

After zip closure

Hook rib
Sliding-hook rib
Bulb rib

Preformed sheet-metal panel

Bulb rib complete with anti-siphon groove

Approx. 60 mm (2-1/2 in.)

Hook rib

FIGURE 16
FASTENERS FOR METAL ROOFING,
SLIDING-HOOK-CLIPS SYSTEM

Section 4.2 Roof Structure
INTRODUCTION

The roof structure must provide a solid and stable base for the roofing materials. It consists of the structural members, including rafters, trusses, and the roof decking.

A variety of structural problems can affect the performance and the longevity of the roofing materials. Movement of the decking, sagging of the decking, movement around openings, movement at connections, and expansion or swelling of the decking or sheathing can all affect the roofing materials. Proper attention to details and design can usually resolve these problems.

The performance of the roofing materials can also affect the roof structure. Excessive moisture in the roof cavity or attic can cause the structural members and the roof decking to deteriorate. This moisture can come from leaks in the roofing materials, from ice damming, or from the interior of the house.

Better building techniques, such as more insulation and tighter air barriers, can significantly improve the energy efficiency of the house and reduce the occurrence of such problems as moisture in the attic.

4.2.1 STRUCTURAL DETERIORATION AND DAMAGE
PROBLEM
SAGGING OF THE ROOF SHEATHING

CAUSE

Inadequate support for the roof sheathing

Roof sheathing that has inadequate edge support can have many shortcomings: it can lead to deflection from wind loading or people walking on the roof and to the distortion or separation of roofing materials.

SOLUTIONS

Install plywood roof sheathing with the face grain perpendicular to the rafters or trusses. Support and secure panel edges adequately.

◆ Install strandboard, waferboard, and plywood with the face grain at right angles to the roof framing.

◆ When using panel-type sheathing of less than 12 mm (1/2 in.) on rafters or trusses at 600 mm (24 in.) o.c., support panel edges between rafters or trusses with H-clips installed at the midpoint between rafters or trusses or with 38 x 38-mm (2 x 2-in.) blocking nailed between rafters or trusses (see Figure 17).

◆ Fasten all sheathing panels along rafters or trusses at 300 mm (12 in.) o.c., and edge fasten them at 150 mm (6 in.) o.c. where they are edge supported.

◆ Boards used as roof sheathing cannot be more than 286 mm (11 in.) wide. Support all lumber ends on solid framing, and stagger end joints.

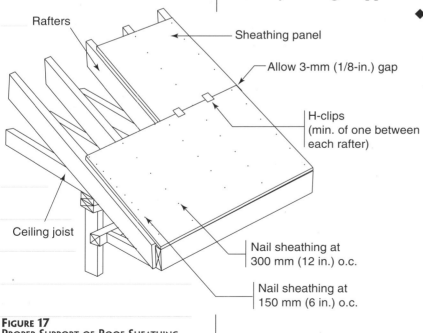

Rafters

Sheathing panel

Allow 3-mm (1/8-in.) gap

H-clips
(min. of one between
each rafter)

Ceiling joist

Nail sheathing at
300 mm (12 in.) o.c.

Nail sheathing at
150 mm (6 in.) o.c.

FIGURE 17
PROPER SUPPORT OF ROOF SHEATHING

PROBLEM
SAGGING OF ROOF SHEATHING

CAUSE

Sheathing materials too thin to support concrete or clay tile roofing

The NBC requirement for panel type sheathing thickness is 9.5 mm (3/8 in.) when support spacing is 600 mm (24 in.). This thickness will support design dead and live loads but may allow deflections which cause a poor appearance.

SOLUTIONS

Reduce spacing of trusses and rafters.

◆ To reduce deflection of roof sheathing, you may decrease the spacing of roof supports from 600 mm (24 in.) to 400 mm (16 in.) o.c.

Increase thickness of roof sheathing.

◆ You may also reduce deflection by increasing the sheathing thickness beyond NBC minimums (see Table 1).

Maximum Spacing of Supports mm (in.)	Minimum Thickness of Roof Sheathing, mm (in.)				
	Plywood and OSB, O-2 Grade		OSB, O-1 Grade and Waferboard, R-1 Grade		Lumber
	Edges Supported	Edges Unsupported	Edges Supported	Edges Unsupported	
300 (12)	7.5 (5/16)	7.5 (5/16)	9.5 (3/8)	9.5 (3/8)	17.0 (11/16)
400 (16)	7.5 (5/16)	9.5 (3/8)	9.5 (3/8)	11.1 (7/16)	17.0 (11/16)
600 (24)	9.5 (3/8)	12.7 (1/2)	11.1 (7/16)	12.7 (1/2)	19.0 (3/4)

Table 1
Minimum Roof Sheathing Thickness

PROBLEM
SAGGING OF THE ROOF SUPPORT STRUCTURE AROUND OPENINGS

CAUSE

Inadequate framing around openings in roofs

Incorrect or inadequate framing around openings for skylights can result in sagging of the structure.

SOLUTIONS

Frame openings to allow for proper transferring of loads.

◆ Whenever a rafter must be cut to provide space for a skylight, frame the roof structure properly to allow for adequate load transfer.

◆ When a rafter is cut, double rafters should be installed on each side of the skylight area. Place double headers between the double rafters, and securely fasten cut rafters into the double headers. Joist hangers can be used to connect cut rafters to the double headers. The headers will transfer the loads from the cut rafters to the adjoining rafters (see Figure 18).

◆ Trusses should not be notched or cut without the truss manufacturer's shop drawings and instructions to ensure that loads are sufficiently transferred.

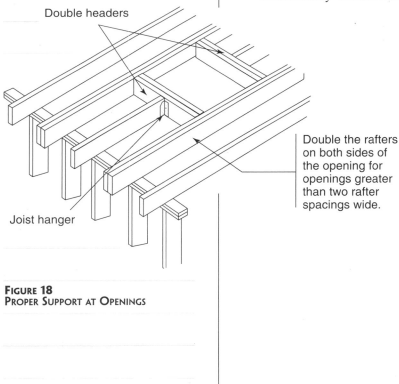

Double headers

Joist hanger

Double the rafters on both sides of the opening for openings greater than two rafter spacings wide.

FIGURE 18
PROPER SUPPORT AT OPENINGS

PROBLEM
ROOF STRUCTURE SAGS AROUND TRUSS CONNECTIONS

CAUSE

Inadequate supports and poor fastening of connections

The use of the wrong type or size of connectors, improper fastening of connectors to truss members, and undersized support beams or girder trusses can all result in sagging of the roof structure under snow loads.

SOLUTIONS

Follow truss roof design for supports and connections.

◆ Roof designs and structures are becoming more complicated. Truss manufacturers provide detailed installation drawings which specify connection types and fastening requirements for all trusses. The strength of truss roof systems depends on the connections being made properly.

◆ Use truss hangers that are large enough, and fully fasten them to support trusses or beams (see Figure 19).

◆ Adequately nail connections that do not require special connectors. Take care not to damage or split truss chords by using poor toe-nailing techniques.

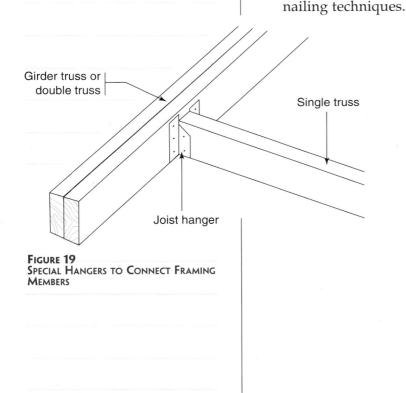

Girder truss or double truss

Single truss

Joist hanger

FIGURE 19
SPECIAL HANGERS TO CONNECT FRAMING MEMBERS

PROBLEM
SHEATHING PANELS RISE UP AT JOINTS, CAUSING RIDGING

CAUSE

Roof panels installed too tightly

Panel sheathing products are often used to "square" the roof and as such are installed with the ends of the panels placed tightly together. When moisture or temperature causes roof sheathing panels to expand, there is no tolerance, resulting in ridging at panel edges.

SOLUTIONS

Space roof panels adequately.

◆ When using strandboard, waferboard, or plywood for roof sheathing, follow the NBC stipulation of a gap between sheets of not less than 2 mm (1/16 in.). Manufacturers of roof sheathing panels may recommend a larger amount of spacing for their own panels. By using some types of H-clips, you automatically ensure an adequate space between panel edges. However, you must provide adequate space along the ends (see Figure 20).

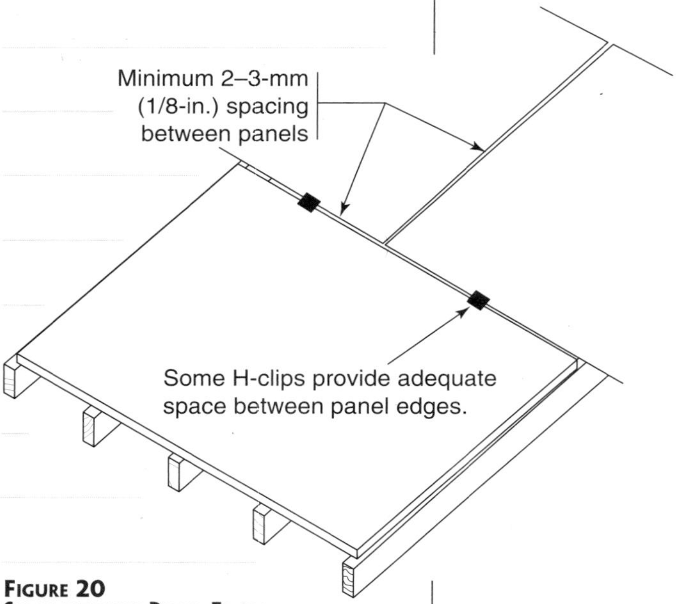

Minimum 2–3-mm (1/8-in.) spacing between panels

Some H-clips provide adequate space between panel edges.

FIGURE 20
SPACE BETWEEN PANEL EDGES

4.2.2 WATER LEAKAGE
PROBLEM
ROTTING OF STRUCTURAL MEMBERS AND SHEATHING MATERIALS

CAUSE

Water leakage due to ice damming

Inadequate eave protection under the roofing can also lead to wet roof sheathing and premature deterioration. Ice dams can trap melt water on the roof above the point where the eave protection ends.

Ice dams are built-up ice at the edge of the roof. Heat escaping from the house melts the snow on the roof. This meltwater flows down the roof until it reaches the outer edge of the eave over the unheated soffit, where it freezes, creating an ice dam. As the ice dam builds up, it stops the flow of meltwater from reaching the eave. This meltwater can back up past the eave protection, wetting the roof sheathing and structural members and leading to rotting.

SOLUTIONS

Install adequate eave protection under roofing materials.

◆ Install eave protection, an impervious roofing strip, at eaves and in valley intersections, to stop water from leaking through the shingles behind ice dams (see Figure 21).

◆ Complicated roof systems that have other roofs draining onto one roof or have direct sun exposure require special attention. Installing an ice and water shield on the roof and under flashings is recommended.

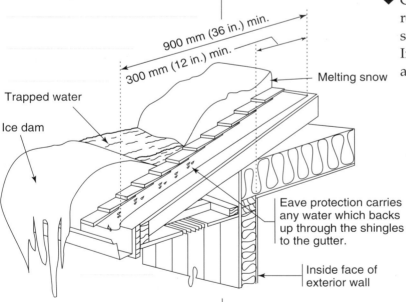

900 mm (36 in.) min.

300 mm (12 in.) min.

Trapped water

Ice dam

Melting snow

Eave protection carries any water which backs up through the shingles to the gutter.

Inside face of exterior wall

FIGURE 21
ICE DAMMING

PROBLEM
ROTTING OF STRUCTURAL MEMBERS AND SHEATHING MATERIALS

CAUSE

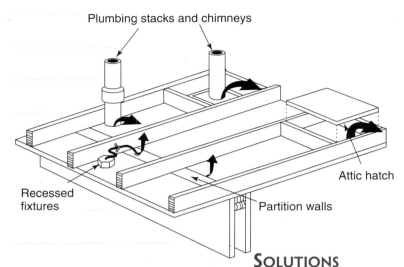

Plumbing stacks and chimneys

Attic hatch

Recessed fixtures

Partition walls

FIGURE 22
AIR LEAKS THAT ALLOW MOISTURE INTO ATTIC

Excessive moisture in the attic space

Wood begins to rot when it reaches a moisture content of 20 percent or greater, and where the ambient temperature is higher than 20°C (68°F). Moisture carried into the attic space can be absorbed by structural members and roof sheathing, creating the conditions necessary for decay. Moisture is carried into the attic space by humid indoor air leaking from the interior of the house (see Figure 22).

SOLUTIONS

Control air leaks to attic space from house.

◆ Reduce the amount of humid indoor air entering the attic by setting up an effective air barrier system between the interior heated space and the attic space. The air barrier system can be made up of polyethylene, solid framing members, sealants, gaskets, wood panels, drywall, and other products. The system must be continuous.

◆ Properly seal penetrations through air barriers, such as at partitions, electrical boxes, and plumbing pipes, by using flexible material to ensure airtightness.

PROBLEM
ROTTING OF STRUCTURAL MEMBERS AND SHEATHING MATERIALS

CAUSE

Water leakage around flashings

When roofing materials are damaged or inadequately flashed, water can leak through, wetting the sheathing and structural members. Constant wetting will result in decay of the sheathing and the structural members.

SOLUTIONS

Roof flashings must be installed properly.

◆ Provide flashing and, where applicable, counterflashing at all intersections between roofs, walls, and chimneys. This will accommodate differential movement between surfaces and prevent the entry of water (see Figure 23).

◆ Follow manufacturers' flashing details for roof vents. Use preformed neoprene flashing for vent pipes.

◆ Flashing should be durable, weather-resistant, and maintenance-free.

◆ Replace or repair damaged materials before you install flashings.

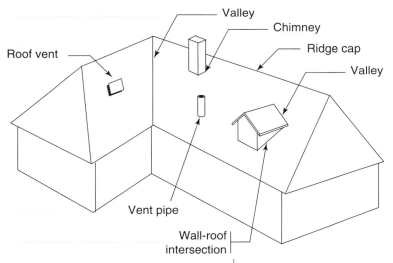

FIGURE 23
FLASHINGS REQUIRED AT ROOF PENETRATIONS

Section 4.3 Interior Finish
INTRODUCTION

Most problems with the interior finish on the ceiling will show up as wet spots, dark spots, cracks, and uneven finishes. Many of these problems relate to the roofing materials or the roof structure.

Cracking of the interior ceiling finish is usually related to the roof structure and, in most cases, to the trusses. There can also be problems with the connections, or with excessive loading in combination with inadequate design.

Wavy ceilings are a result of improper conditions in the house during construction and the scheduling process. Preventing this problem is simple and eliminates difficult and expensive repairs.

Wet spots in the ceiling generally come from two sources: water leaking through the roofing materials; or moisture-laden air leaking from inside the house.

Mold and mildew growth is dealt with in this section. As with many housing problems, techniques for solving other shortcomings will also solve this deficiency. Better building practices and attention to details will generally rectify problems.

4.3.1 STRUCTURAL DETERIORATION AND DAMAGE

PROBLEM
WALL–CEILING SEPARATION

CAUSE

Truss uplift

Differential shrinkage can occur between the top and bottom chords due to temperature and moisture conditions. Because of this, the bottom chord bends upward, pulling the ceiling drywall, and occasionally the interior partitions, with it (see Figure 24).

SOLUTIONS

Minimize moisture in the attic, use kiln-dried lumber for trusses, float drywall corners, use mono trusses in place of full-span trusses, or install resilient channels perpendicular to trusses before you apply drywall (see Figure 25).

◆ The greater the amount of moisture in the attic, the greater the potential for the truss to take on this moisture. Reduce the amount of moisture that enters the attic by using an effective air-barrier system. Ventilation of the attic can also help keep moisture levels under control.

◆ Trusses should be fabricated using kiln-dried wood. Store trusses properly and cover them as soon as they are installed so that they do not take on moisture.

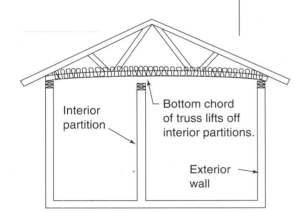

FIGURE 24
WALL–CEILING SEPARATION DUE TO TRUSS UPLIFT

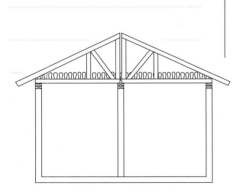

FIGURE 25
USE OF MONO TRUSSES

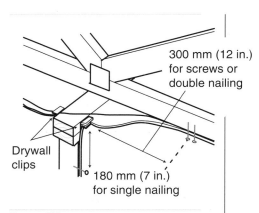

300 mm (12 in.)
for screws or
double nailing

Drywall
clips

180 mm (7 in.)
for single nailing

FIGURE 26
FLOATING DRYWALL CORNER ALONG
PARTITIONS

◆ Floating the corners will hide the effects of truss uplift (see Figure 26). This technique involves keeping the fasteners for both the ceiling drywall and the partition wall drywall away from the corner joint. This uses the natural flexibility of the drywall to allow uplift of 50 to 75 mm (2 to 3 in.) to occur without cracking the corner joint. Recommended float distances are 300 mm (12 in.) for 12-mm (1/2-in.) ceilings; 400 mm (16 in.) for 16-mm (5/8-in.) ceilings; and 200 mm (8 in.) for partition walls. With floating corners, double the first row of fasteners to prevent pull-through. The stress on corner joints can be reduced by holding the ceiling drywall to the top plate with drywall clips, with wood blocks, or with wider top plates and strapping.

PROBLEM
WAVY CEILINGS

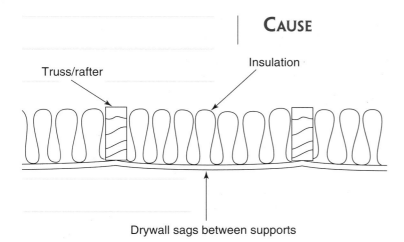

Truss/rafter

Insulation

Drywall sags between supports

FIGURE 27
WET DRYWALL SAGS BETWEEN SUPPORTS

CAUSE

High humidity and water absorption by the ceiling drywall

Water-based finishes are often applied to the ceiling, and if the drywall absorbs a substantial amount of this water, it can sag (see Figure 27). Textured ceilings are common examples.

SOLUTIONS

Use thicker drywall.

◆ Heavier drywall is better able to support itself and the insulation above in elevated moisture conditions. The NBC requires that 16-mm (5/8-in.) gypsum board be used for water-based texture ceilings when supports are 600 mm (24 in.) o.c. Apply the drywall perpendicular to the supports.

◆ You may use controlled-density (CD) or sag-resistant (SR) drywall in place of regular gypsum board.

PROBLEM
WAVY CEILINGS

CAUSE

Excess humidity in the house during construction

High humidity during construction can cause the drywall to take on extra moisture. Construction humidity comes from drying lumber, interior finishing materials, temporary heat (propane), and poured concrete floors.

SOLUTIONS

Properly schedule activities to reduce the amount of humidity present after you have installed the drywall, and ventilate to keep moisture levels low.

◆ Insulate the ceiling immediately after installing the ceiling drywall. Condensation can occur on the upper side of the ceiling drywall during cool or cold weather if the attic is not insulated promptly after the ceiling drywall is installed. Moisture from inside the house will freeze or condense on the vapour barrier above the ceiling drywall. This moisture will then be absorbed by the ceiling drywall and cause it to sag.

◆ Schedule work in the house so that you reduce the amount of moisture present after the drywall is installed. The pouring of concrete floors and other similar activities can introduce large amounts of moisture, which can be absorbed by the drywall and cause it to sag. Do all of these types of activities before you drywall.

◆ Providing plenty of ventilation during construction is critical to keeping humidity levels under control. Literally thousands of litres of water can be introduced into the house from construction materials and temporary unvented heaters. Some of this moisture will be absorbed by the drywall unless the house is continuously ventilated to reduce moisture levels.

4.3.2 WATER LEAKAGE PROBLEM

WET CEILINGS DUE TO ATTIC CONDENSATION

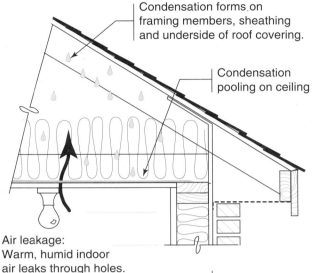

Condensation forms on framing members, sheathing and underside of roof covering.

Condensation pooling on ceiling

Air leakage:
Warm, humid indoor air leaks through holes.

FIGURE 28
WET CEILINGS CAUSED BY ATTIC CONDENSATION

CAUSE

Air leakage

Warm, moist air leaks from the interior of the house into the attic space through gaps in the air barrier. When this moist air enters the cold attic, the moisture freezes onto cold surfaces such as roof sheathing and framing members. When the attic space warms, the ice melts and makes its way back to the ceiling drywall, resulting in wetting and damage (see Figure 28).

SOLUTIONS

Install a continuous air barrier and ventilate the attic.

◆ Air barriers must be continuous with no holes. They reduce the amount of moisture that can make its way into the attic. Positive air pressure at the ceiling level will force moisture-laden air into the attic. Reducing the number of penetrations in the ceiling air barrier will increase the integrity of the air barrier. Employing polyethylene boxes around lighting outlets and gaskets around stacks and vents; eliminating or weatherstripping interior attic accesses; and using acoustic caulking at all joints will substantially improve the air barrier and reduce moisture problems.

◆ Ventilating the attic space will minimize the effects of the moisture that does make its way into the attic. Ventilation allows the attic space to dry out after condensation and melting take place. Providing ventilation in accordance with the NBC and ensuring that insulation stops are installed properly will help minimize moisture problems.

PROBLEM
MOLD AND MILDEW GROWTH

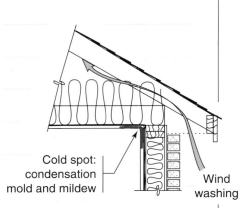

Cold spot: condensation mold and mildew

Wind washing

FIGURE 29
MOLD AND MILDEW CAUSED BY COLD CORNER

CAUSE

Excessive humidity and cold spots

When high humidity levels combine with cold spots on the wall or ceiling, the result can be mold and mildew growth. People find higher humidity levels more comfortable and often humidify their houses. Cold spots in corners where ceilings meet walls can occur due to inadequate insulation and wind washing. This provides an ideal environment for mold growth (see Figure 29).

SOLUTIONS

Increase ventilation to control humidity. Insulate properly and reduce wind washing.

◆ Keep humidity levels low enough to prevent condensation on windows during winter months. You may also attain higher humidity levels by using improved wall and ceiling construction and high-efficiency windows.

◆ Increase the amount of insulation over the exterior walls, and ensure that the insulation goes right to the exterior of the outside walls. The use of high heel trusses will allow for greater depths of insulation to be installed at the outside walls.

◆ Use insulation stops. These baffles prevent cold air from blowing the insulation out of place, and they also keep the air from short-circuiting through the insulation. If air is moving through the insulation, it reduces the effectiveness of the insulation and creates a cold spot (see Figure 30).

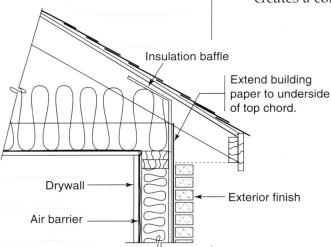

Insulation baffle

Extend building paper to underside of top chord.

Drywall

Air barrier

Exterior finish

FIGURE 30
PROPER CONSTRUCTION OF CORNER

Section 4.4 Additional Reading

SOURCE	PUBLICATION
Canada Mortgage and Housing Corporation 700 Montreal Road Ottawa ON K1A 0P7 613 748-2367	*Canadian Wood-Frame House Construction*, 1997 NHA 5031
Council of Forest Industries of B.C. 1200-555 Burrard Street Vancouver BC V7X 1S7 604 684-0211	*Western Red Cedar Shingles and Shakes—A Handbook of Good Practice*, 1987
	The Western Red Cedar Handbook, 1987
	Roof and Wall Shingling Made Easy, 1987
National Research Council of Canada Institute for Research in Construction Publications Section Ottawa ON K1A 0R6 In Ottawa: 613 993-2463 Other locations: 1 800 672-7990	*The Difference Between a Vapour Barrier and an Air Barrier*, 1985 BPN 54
	Humidity, Condensation, Ventilation in Houses, 1984 NRCC 23293
	Vapour Barriers: What Are They? Are They Effective? 1976 CBD 176
	Moisture Problems in Houses, 1984 CBD 231
Canadian Home Builders' Association 150 Laurier Avenue West, Suite 500 Ottawa ON K1P 5J4 613 230-3060	*CHBA Builders' Manual*, 1994
The Canadian Wood Truss Association 1400 Blair Place, Suite 210 Ottawa ON K1J 9B8	

CHAPTER 5

Introduction

INDOOR AIR QUALITY AND VENTILATION

This chapter aims to apprise builders of the challenges and problems that indoor air quality and improper ventilation present. It gives you practical advice on

- how to build for good indoor air quality;
- how to provide make-up air and good exhaust systems;
- how to operate a house for high indoor air quality; and
- how to solve indoor air-quality problems if they occur.

Good indoor air quality can be defined as the control of any substance that is a health hazard, a source of discomfort to the occupants, or a threat to the building structure. Health hazards and sources of discomfort will, naturally, vary from person to person. This chapter provides information that applies to the general public.

Hypersensitive people—those with unusual sensitivity to allergens or chemicals—may require special types of housing not covered in this guide. You should anticipate that your clients may be sensitive and that they may not recognize it until after they have moved into their new house. For information on the needs of hypersensitive people, refer to the publications listed at the back of this guide, and consult CMHC, allergists, and indoor air-quality specialists.

Every builder can benefit from up-to-date information on indoor air quality. The reasons are many:

- ◆ Canadians, on average, spend 90 percent of their time in buildings (fewer than two and a half hours a day outdoors). Much of that time is spent in their home, but schools, offices, factories, and malls are also buildings where people pass parts of their days.

- ◆ There is a much greater awareness now than there once was about the need for a healthy lifestyle. A healthy indoor environment is part of that lifestyle.

- ◆ Synthetic construction materials introduce large amounts of chemicals into houses, especially over the first year or two. Exposed materials may emit varying levels of VOCs and formaldehyde gas. Caulking and sealants can generate toxic compounds.

- ◆ The use of panel or sheet construction materials, upgraded air barrier systems, better sealants, and tighter doors and windows is leading to the construction of tighter houses. Without adequate attention to ventilation and pollution control, indoor air quality can be a significant problem.

♦ The use of large-capacity exhaust fans can create indoor air-quality problems by causing combustion appliances to backdraft or by pulling radon and other soil gases into the house.

For the knowledgeable builder, good indoor air quality provides a wide range of opportunities.

♦ More features
- cleaner air: healthier homes
- lower dust levels: reduced need for cleaning
- controlled humidity levels: improved comfort
- reduced potential for condensation: greater durability
- better ventilation: improved control

♦ Home-owner confidence
- factual answers to indoor air-quality questions
- builder-generated solutions to indoor air-quality problems

♦ Fewer problems
- more durable construction because humidity levels and moisture problems are reduced
- greater comfort
- a safer home environment

By applying the principles outlined in this chapter, you can produce a more durable house, which is less prone to moisture and rot problems, thus reducing callbacks.

Section 5.1 Source Control
INTRODUCTION

FIGURE 1
SOME SOURCES OF POLLUTANTS

Source control is the cornerstone of a good indoor air-quality strategy. Through careful design and selection of materials, you can greatly reduce the number and levels of contaminants to which occupants of the home will be exposed. The following section of the guide provides an overview of source control strategies that are available to the builder. The section discusses the following contaminants:

◆ soil gases: radon, methane, and water vapour;

◆ outdoor pollutants;

◆ formaldehyde and volatile organic compounds (VOCs);

◆ particulates;

◆ wood smoke;

◆ flue gases from gas fireplaces and ranges;

◆ flue gases from furnaces, boilers, and water heaters; and

◆ mold and mildew.

5.1.1 SOIL GASES—RADON AND WATER VAPOUR

Various gases can enter a house through the foundation (see Figure 2). These range from water vapour, which is the most common, to the more difficult radon (a radioactive gas), methane, and pesticides. Mold from the soil, while not a gas, also enters through the foundation; mold aggravates allergies and, in some cases, causes more serious health problems, as can soil gases.

Many problems can be avoided before construction by choosing not to build on wet sites, or sites on or near old sanitary landfills. Radon varies a great deal from site to site, and its presence cannot be reliably detected before construction. Even in parts of the country where radon is not recognized to be a problem, builders should take note of the radon-control techniques designed to reduce the entry of soil gas. The 1995 National Building Code of Canada (NBC) incorporates radon- and soil-gas-control techniques.

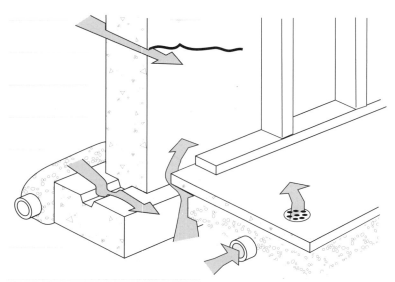

FIGURE 2
SOIL GAS ENTRY POINTS IN A BASEMENT FOUNDATION

PROBLEM
HIGH HUMIDITY IN BASEMENT AREAS AND CRAWL SPACES WITH ACCOMPANYING ODOURS, AND MOLD AND MILDEW GROWTH

CAUSE

Movement of water vapour through cracks and penetrations in the foundation slab and walls, and through the concrete slab and foundation walls by capillary action.

SOLUTIONS

◆ Keep water in the soil away from foundation walls through the use of drainage membranes, free-draining insulation materials, or a granular drainage layer.

◆ Minimize cracking of the concrete slab by using a dry mix and plasticizers.

◆ Provide a continuous layer of 0.15-mm (6-mil) or cross-laminated polyethylene beneath the slab to minimize the movement of soil moisture.

◆ Seal any cracks and gaps in floors, walls, and openings caused by plumbing, electrical conduit, and steel post penetrations through the concrete. Use appropriate sealants, such as one-part urethane, after the concrete has cured.

◆ When placing a wood subfloor, seal the concrete slab with 0.15-mm (6-mil) polyethylene sheeting beneath the sleepers.

◆ Provide a moisture barrier to the interior face of concrete walls from slab to grade level. Use polyethylene, but do not extend the material above ground level.

CAUSE

High water table beneath the slab and adjacent to walls.

SOLUTIONS

◆ Do not build below the high water table.

◆ Place floor slab on a drainage pad of crushed rock (containing no more than 10 percent of material which will pass through a 4-mm [1/8-in.] sieve) on soil sloped to a centrally located sump.

◆ The drainage layer must be at least 125 mm (5 in.) thick; it should be greater where wet soil becomes mixed with the granular drainage material.

◆ Run perimeter drainage around footings, and tie it into storm sewers or run it to a dry well or sump pit.

◆ Backfill with porous material, or use a drainage mat or drainage-type rigid fibreglass insulation connected to the drain tile.

PROBLEM

HIGH RADON READINGS IN THE HOUSE

CAUSE

Soil-gas entry through cracks in foundation walls and slabs

SOLUTIONS

◆ As per the NBC, seal all cracks, gaps, and penetrations in the foundation walls and slab. Provide a continuous layer of 0.15-mm (6-mil) polyethylene beneath the slab, lapped at least 300 mm (12 in.) (see Figure 3).

◆ Build a continuous air barrier at the interior finish. Refer to Chapter 1, "Foundations."

◆ When radon levels are known, or expected to be high, slightly pressurize the basement, or install a sub-slab depressurization system.

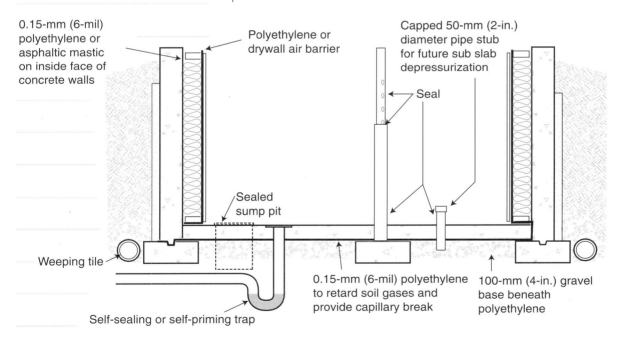

0.15-mm (6-mil) polyethylene or asphaltic mastic on inside face of concrete walls

Polyethylene or drywall air barrier

Capped 50-mm (2-in.) diameter pipe stub for future sub slab depressurization

Seal

Sealed sump pit

Weeping tile

Self-sealing or self-priming trap

0.15-mm (6-mil) polyethylene to retard soil gases and provide capillary break

100-mm (4-in.) gravel base beneath polyethylene

FIGURE 3
CONTROLLING THE ENTRY OF SOIL GASES INTO A BASEMENT FOUNDATION

CAUSE

Soil gas entry through floor drains, sumps, and the weeping tile system

SOLUTIONS

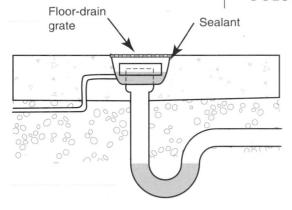

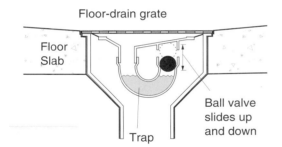

FIGURE 4
SELF-SEALING FLOOR

◆ Use self-priming floor traps.

◆ Use self-sealing floor traps (see Figure 4). This is especially important if the weeping tiles connect to the floor drain above the trap.

◆ Seal sump covers to reduce water vapour and radon entry. Install submersible pumps which can operate in an enclosed environment.

5.1.2 OUTDOOR POLLUTANTS

Outdoor air in certain locations carries with it pollutants that affect both the house and the occupants. Pollutants resulting from human activity, such as car exhaust, industrial air pollution, and wood smoke, may cause headaches and poisoning, and aggravate chemical sensitivities. Natural pollutants such as pollen, dust, and mold may cause allergic reactions.

The house location has a significant effect on the entry of outdoor air pollutants. Outdoor air around sites adjacent to busy streets has a higher car exhaust content, especially when the site is close to stop signs, traffic lights or bus stops. Sites near industrial facilities are more likely to suffer from industrial pollutants. Wood smoke can be carried around the house on wind currents and can infiltrate through the building envelope or can be drawn into the house through make-up air intakes. Areas in which temperature inversions occur are likely to have higher levels of all pollutants.

PROBLEM

ENTRY OF OUTDOOR AIR POLLUTANTS AND CONTAMINANTS

CAUSE

Poor location and filtration of incoming ventilation air

SOLUTIONS

Locate outdoor air intakes to minimize drawing contaminants into the house.

◆ Avoid areas where exhaust or spillage from ventilation systems, gas meters, and fuel-burning appliances might be drawn back into the building.

◆ Avoid locations close to driveways or areas where vehicles might be idling.

◆ Avoid locations where organic matter (grass clippings, leaves, etc.) or pesticides and fertilizers are likely to be drawn into the intake vent.

◆ The intake system must be at least 450 mm (18 in.) above the ground and, at a minimum, above the highest winter snow level (generally, the higher it is located, the better). Proper screening is required to prevent rodents and insects from entering the home.

Provide filtration of exterior intake air to minimize the entry of dust and pollen. Dust, pollen, and odours can be brought in by the intake air. To minimize these contaminants, filters can be incorporated in the return air plenum of the forced-air system. Note that most filters remove only particulates, not gases or odours. Various kinds of filters or combinations of filters may be required, such as

- low-efficiency fibreglass filters for filtering out large items like insects;

- medium-efficiency pleated fabric filters rated at 40 to 60 percent;

- high-efficiency filters (HEPA) for filtering out dust and pollen;

- electrostatic filters for removing smoke and smaller particles; and

- activated carbon filters for removing odours and many other gases (not effective for carbon monoxide). These carbon filters cannot be relied upon as they can get saturated easily if the bed is not deep enough.

Incorporate higher-efficiency filtration into forced-air furnaces.

◆ HEPA and activated charcoal filters represent high-end options and will require the fabrication of specially sized filter slots in the furnace ductwork. They are most easily installed with the ductwork. The fans must be sized to accommodate the higher pressure drop of HEPA filters.

◆ As a minimum, consider using medium-efficiency (60 percent) pleated fabric filters, 50 mm (2 in.) thick. The thicker the filter, the greater the filtering area and the less often the home-owner will need to replace the filter. Advise home-owners to inspect and replace filters as required.

CAUSE

Uncontrolled entry of outdoor air through cracks and openings in exterior walls, floors, and ceilings.

SOLUTIONS

◆ Construct the house with a continuous air-barrier system (see Figure 5). Air-barrier systems are described in detail in CMHC's *Canadian Wood-Frame House Construction.*

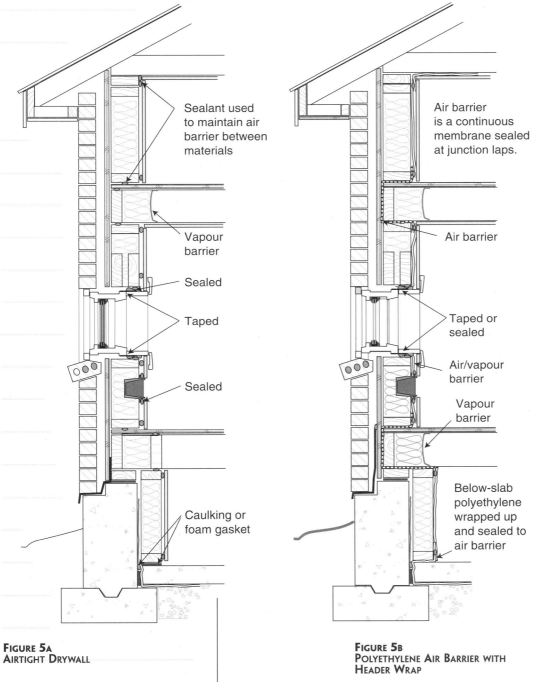

Sealant used to maintain air barrier between materials

Vapour barrier

Sealed

Taped

Sealed

Caulking or foam gasket

FIGURE 5A
AIRTIGHT DRYWALL

Air barrier is a continuous membrane sealed at junction laps.

Air barrier

Taped or sealed

Air/vapour barrier

Vapour barrier

Below-slab polyethylene wrapped up and sealed to air barrier

FIGURE 5B
POLYETHYLENE AIR BARRIER WITH HEADER WRAP

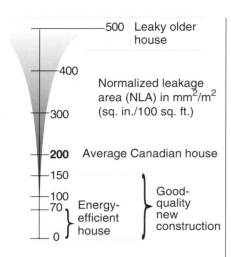

FIGURE 6
INTERPRETING THE RESULTS OF A
FAN-DOOR TEST

A house depressurization test can be performed to validate envelope tightness. This test measures the sum of the areas of all holes and cracks in the building skin; this area is called the equivalent leakage area, or ELA. The ELA can be divided by the outside surface area of the building to give the average leakage area (called the normalized leakage area, or NLA) for every square metre. An effective air-barrier system exists when a house has an NLA of 155 mm^2/m^2 (2 sq. in./100 sq. ft.) or less when tested at 50 Pa (see Figure 6).

◆ Install doors and opening windows that seal tightly.

5.1.3 FORMALDEHYDE AND VOCS

Formaldehyde gas can be released by formaldehyde-based glues. Urea formaldehyde glues are widely used in construction products such as particleboards, some types of insulation, interior panelling, furniture, carpeting, and drapery. Urea formaldehyde adhesives are less stable than phenol-based formaldehyde. Formaldehyde gas is colourless, with a strong pungent odour at elevated levels. It can cause headaches, stinging eyes, and strong allergic reactions in some people. Offgassing of formaldehyde dissipates within the first few years of occupancy.

Formaldehyde gas can be released from carpets and other synthetic fabrics such as upholstery, and will be emitted for a period of time from durable-press fabrics. Formaldehyde is also an ingredient of ureaformaldehyde glues in non structural wood panels used for cabinetry, furniture and decorative paneling.

PROBLEM
OFFGASSING OF FORMALDEHYDE

CAUSE

Formaldehyde and VOCs may be given off by some materials.

SOLUTIONS

◆ Use panels with the more stable phenol formaldehyde glues, or other adhesive types such as isocyanate or polyvinyl acetate.

◆ Seal edges or faces which do not have a laminate or melamine finish.

◆ Ventilate the house before the owners move in.

◆ Install a mechanical ventilation system controlled by a dehumidistat to allow homeowners to regulate humidity levels in the house. A dehumidifier can be used if humidity levels are above 60 percent.

◆ Select furnishings that have low formaldehyde emissions.

◆ Select carpets with low formaldehyde content.

◆ Purchase panels that are labeled or stamped to be in conformance with standards that specify lower formaldehyde emission levels. Consult your manufacturer and the National Building Code for appropriate grades.

Many building materials, such as paints, caulking, and glues, release organic solvents when curing. This process can last many months, during which the organic vapours may cause a number of symptoms, such as headaches, allergic reactions, and bronchial irritation. Some of these solvents are known to cause long-term health problems.

PROBLEM
RELEASE OF ORGANIC SOLVENTS FROM BUILDING MATERIALS IN THE HOUSE

CAUSE

Curing of new materials

SOLUTIONS

◆ Select low-toxicity sealants and finishing materials. Refer to CMHC's *Building Materials for the Environmentally Hypersensitive*.

◆ Avoid indoor use of exterior-grade sealants.

◆ Ventilate the house continuously at a high rate before occupancy.

◆ Providing heat and plenty of ventilation will accelerate the release of organic vapours during this breaking-in period. Temperatures should not be set too high to prevent deterioration of materials.

◆ New carpets are a source of volatile chemical contaminants. Using less carpet in the home will result in better indoor air quality.

PROBLEM
RELEASE OF ORGANIC VAPOURS FROM CLEANING AGENTS, PAINTS, AND SOLVENTS

CAUSE

Storage and use inside the house

SOLUTIONS

◆ Never use paint strippers indoors.

◆ Educate home-owners about the need to ventilate when using cleaning agents, paints, and solvents.

◆ To store volatile chemicals, provide cupboards that have weather-stripped doors and are vented to the outside. Use self-closing devices on cupboard doors. Ensure that the cupboard vents will not act as air intakes.

5.1.4 PARTICULATES

The term "particulates" refers to small particles that are suspended in the air and can be inhaled. High levels of particulates can cause respiratory problems. Dust, pollen, fungal spores, and mites aggravate allergies. Bacteria and viruses thrive at either low or high humidity. Mineral fibres cause irritation to the skin, eyes, and lungs. Smoke particles are particularly harmful in that they are quite small and therefore penetrate deep into the lungs.

PROBLEM

EXCESSIVE PARTICULATES IN THE INDOOR AIR

CAUSE

Construction debris and dust circulating through the house

Circulation of lint and dust throughout the dwelling

SOLUTIONS

◆ Cover duct outlets and floor-plate openings during construction, and clean the duct system before the owners move in.

◆ Install a high-efficiency filtration system (see section 5.1.2).

◆ Provide vents for the clothes dryer that exhaust lint to the outdoors.

◆ Install a central vacuum system that exhausts to the outdoors.

PROBLEM
CONVENTIONAL VACUUMS TEND TO SEND FINE PARTICLES INTO THE HOUSE AIR

CAUSE

Occupants' lifestyle (for example, smoking, types of furnishings, pets, hobbies [pottery, woodworking, etc.])

SOLUTIONS

◆ Install a high-efficiency filtration system (see section 5.1.2).

◆ Provide for continuous ventilation at a low rate.

Increased air circulation promotes "plating out" of suspended particles onto floors and furnishings, making removal easier through cleaning and vacuuming.

◆ Provide improved control over humidity with humidistats, furnace humidifiers, dehumidistats, exhaust fans, and so on. Educate home-owners regarding the optimum range of humidity levels (30 to 45 percent) to control bacteria, viruses, and mites.

5.1.5 WOOD SMOKE FROM FIREPLACES AND WOOD STOVES

Wood smoke contains many pollutants. Of greatest concern is carbon monoxide, which can cause poisoning and death; combustion particles, like soot, which can cause bronchial irritation; and complex hydrocarbons or aromatic hydrocarbons, which can cause cancer. The risks of carbon monoxide poisoning are increased when a solid-fuel burning appliance is left to "burn out." As the fire burns to embers and coals, the flue cools, allowing more cool air to come down the chimney and spill out of the appliance into the house.

PROBLEM

CIRCULATION OF WOOD COMBUSTION BY-PRODUCTS (SMOKE AND PARTICULATES) THROUGHOUT THE HOUSE

CAUSE

Uncertified or poorly constructed and installed wood-burning appliances

SOLUTIONS

◆ Keep chimneys inside the house envelope. Running the chimney to the roof inside the house (as opposed to up the outside wall) helps prevent the chimney from becoming cold as the fire dies down.

◆ It is strongly recommended that wood-burning appliances installed in new housing meet CSA B415.1-M92 or the U.S. Environmental Protection Agency (EPA) wood-burning appliance standards (1990), CFR Part 60.

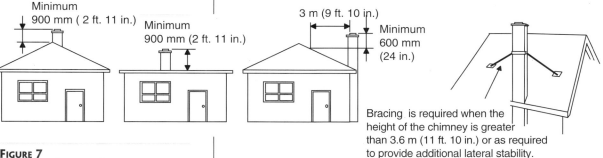

Minimum 900 mm (2 ft. 11 in.)

Minimum 900 mm (2 ft. 11 in.)

3 m (9 ft. 10 in.)

Minimum 600 mm (24 in.)

Bracing is required when the height of the chimney is greater than 3.6 m (11 ft. 10 in.) or as required to provide additional lateral stability.

FIGURE 7
HEIGHT OF CHIMNEY FLUES

Equipment certified to CSA or EPA standards will more completely burn up wood fuels, resulting in greater heat production and cleaner emissions. There is less backdrafting and spillage from this equipment, if it is properly installed, than there is from uncertified products.

◆ It is not necessary to directly supply combustion air to newer wood-burning appliances. However, in houses with high-volume exhaust equipment, make-up air to alleviate significant pressure may be required where soil gas is deemed to be a problem.

◆ CMHC studies have demonstrated that glass doors, even if not tight-fitting, can reduce the possibility of carbon monoxide's entering the home.

◆ Ensure that chimney projection above the roof line meets NBC minimums (see Figure 7).

◆ Install a draft-inducing flue cap (see Figure 8).

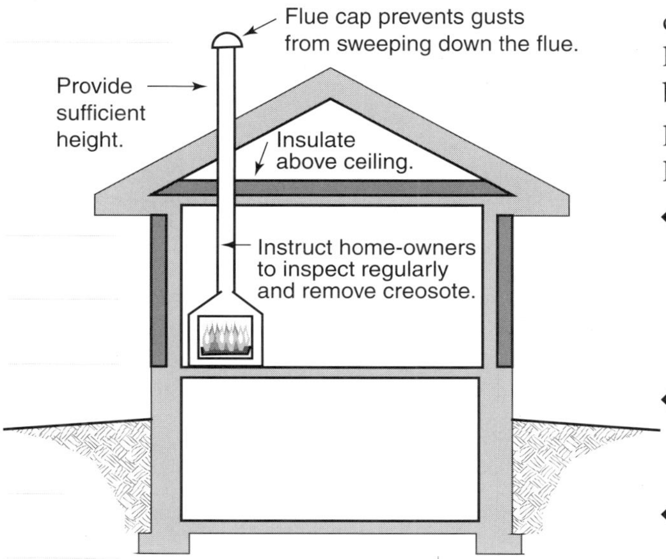

Flue cap prevents gusts from sweeping down the flue.

Provide sufficient height.

Insulate above ceiling.

Instruct home-owners to inspect regularly and remove creosote.

FIGURE 8
DRAFT-INDUCING FLUE CAP

5.1.6 FLUE GASES FROM GAS FIREPLACES AND GAS RANGES

Gas ranges produce large amounts of combustion products which, unless adequately vented, can have adverse effects on the occupants. Gas ranges produce nitrogen dioxide and carbon monoxide. These can cause headaches and allergic reactions in some people.

Gas logs and gas fireplace inserts in masonry fireplaces are becoming more common in Canadian housing. Despite safety measures taken by manufacturers and testing agencies, the potential for flue-gas spillage still exists. Houses are becoming progressively more airtight, and larger exhaust fans without adequate make-up air create negative pressures and induce spillage from gas fireplaces.

When flue gases spill, they typically produce excessively high levels of nitrogen dioxide, which can damage lungs and increase susceptibility to colds and other respiratory problems. Carbon monoxide may also be present; it can lead to headaches, nausea, and death. Large amounts of water vapour are dumped into the house when flues spill.

PROBLEM
LINGERING COMBUSTION BY-PRODUCTS FROM GAS RANGES

CAUSE

Spillage of combustion by-products into the home

SOLUTIONS

◆ Install gas stoves with pilot-light-linked electronic ignition to reduce gas emissions.

◆ Build vertical surfaces around the range to direct the gas plume to the exhaust hood.

◆ Ensure that the range hood exhausts to the outside, or purchase ranges with built-in exhaust systems.

PROBLEM
SPILLAGE OF FLUE GASES FROM GAS FIREPLACES

CAUSE

Combustion process not sealed from the house

SOLUTIONS

◆ Install a sealed-combustion gas fireplace which draws combustion air directly from the outside through a concentric flue, completely isolating the combustion process from the house. These units must be located on an outside wall (see Figure 9).

◆ Combustion air feed to a gas fireplace will help reduce, but may not entirely eliminate, spillage.

To eliminate the potential for spillage in houses having exhaust devices with capacities greater than 75 L/s (150 cfm), the ventilation systems must be designed to provide adequate make-up air when the exhaust devices are working.

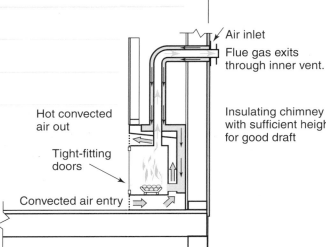

Air inlet

Flue gas exits through inner vent.

Hot convected air out

Insulating chimney flue with sufficient height for good draft

Tight-fitting doors

Convected air entry

FIGURE 9
ZERO-CLEARANCE FIREPLACE WITH OUTSIDE COMBUSTION AIR FEED

5.1.7 MOLD AND MILDEW

In addition to causing odours and staining, mold and mildew on interior finishes can also bring on allergic reactions in some people. There is increasing evidence, too, that certain types of mold release mycotoxins, which can cause very serious health problems. These health difficulties arise mainly from the airborne spores that established mold produces. Since mold and mildew need moisture to grow, fungi are best controlled by eliminating wet surfaces.

PROBLEM
MOLD AND MILDEW GROWTH

CAUSE

Poor insulation at exterior wall corners, wall and ceiling junctions, and in finished basements

Moisture condenses on these cold surfaces, providing an environment suitable for the growth of mold and mildew.

SOLUTIONS

◆ Raise the surface temperature of the drywall by providing better insulation in corners and where ceiling framing members or trusses rest on outside walls. This can be done by insulating the stud "gutter" at outside corners during framing, or by using two-stud framing with drywall clips, which can be insulated with the rest of the wall (see Figure 10). The use of exterior insulating sheathing also reduces thermal bridges at corners.

◆ Insulate the ceiling or wall joint, but be sure that it can still provide adequate attic ventilation. This can be done with baffles and a raised-heel truss (see Figure 11).

Insulation placed between studs before wall sheathing

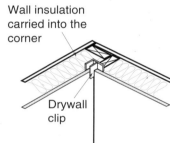

Wall insulation carried into the corner

Drywall clip

FIGURE 10
EXTERIOR CORNER INSULATION

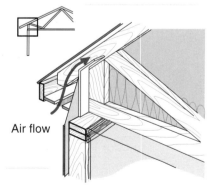

Air flow

FIGURE 11
RAISED-HEEL TRUSS

PROBLEM
MOLD AND MILDEW GROWTH

CAUSE

High indoor humidity levels

This can be caused by the following moisture sources: drying construction materials, damp basements, infiltration of moist air from below grade, seasonal storage of moisture in the building and its contents, and the occupants' activities. In the first year, up to 2 250 litres (500 gallons) of water can be released as the house dries.

SOLUTIONS

◆ Reduce moisture sources.

  – Apply moisture-control principles when constructing the foundation to reduce moisture input from surrounding soils (see Figure 12). Refer to Chapter 1, "Foundations."

◆ Provide dehumidification through better ventilation and by controlling the operation of bathroom exhaust fans with a dehumidistat set at 45 percent relative humidity (RH) or less. Ensure that the fan is capable of continuous mechanical operation and has a low noise rating. Provide tempering for make-up air.

◆ Tell home-owners about moisture-generating activities and the proper use of humidifiers and exhaust fans. Set the dehumidistat below 45 percent RH.

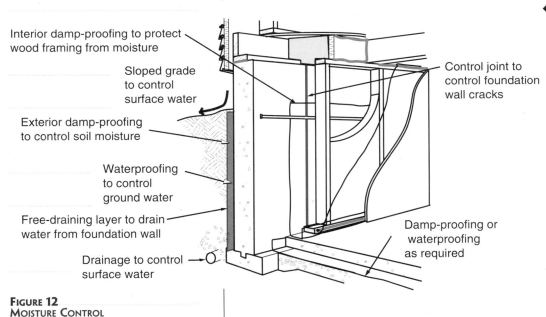

Interior damp-proofing to protect wood framing from moisture

Sloped grade to control surface water

Exterior damp-proofing to control soil moisture

Waterproofing to control ground water

Free-draining layer to drain water from foundation wall

Drainage to control surface water

Control joint to control foundation wall cracks

Damp-proofing or waterproofing as required

FIGURE 12
MOISTURE CONTROL

CAUSE

Poorly maintained mechanical equipment

Humidifiers, dehumidifiers, air-conditioning units, and heat-recovery ventilators can become breeding grounds for mold.

SOLUTIONS

◆ Educate home-owners on the need for proper cleaning and regular maintenance of all equipment that contains water.

PROBLEM
EXCESSIVE CONDENSATION ON WINDOWS

Moisture will condense from warm house air when it comes into contact with cooler surfaces. The combination of a cold interior glass surface and high indoor humidity levels will result in condensation. The temperature of the interior surface of the glass is determined by the thermal properties of the window unit and the flow of warm air over the glass. Condensation can result in damage to interior finishes and can foster the development of mold and mildew.

CAUSE

Cold surfaces and high humidity

SOLUTIONS

◆ Install windows with improved thermal performance (Low E, gas fills, insulated spacers).

◆ Install windows with low air-leakage characteristics.

◆ Insulate and air seal the shim space.

CAUSE

Insufficient delivery of warm, dry air to windows and corners.

SOLUTIONS

◆ Ensure supply air is provided at adequate volume and velocity.

◆ Direct warm air registers at potential condensation problem areas.

◆ Undercut doors at least 10 mm (3/8 in.) above finish flooring to promote improved circulation, or provide return-air duct inlets.

◆ Mount windows closer to the interior faces of walls.

◆ Advise home-owners to avoid excessive thermostat setbacks.

◆ Remove blinds that are installed to fit in window openings.

◆ Hang curtains so as to permit air flow between walls and windows.

Section 5.2 Exhaust Systems and Make-up Air
INTRODUCTION

Removing contaminants from inside the building is the second-best strategy, after source control, for improving indoor air quality. An exhaust system is designed to convey air from inside a house directly to the outdoors. It consists of a fan, interconnecting ductwork, and a termination device.

The purpose of an exhaust system is

◆ to remove air contaminants at their source; and

◆ to control humidity.

Typically, exhaust fans in the home are located in bathrooms and kitchens. While these fans are intended to effectively remove moisture and odours from the home, all too often deficiencies in installation and operation restrict their ability to perform the required function. Field studies have found that only one range-hood installation out of 20 tested exhausted the amount of air for which the fan was rated. Most operated at 15 to 50 percent of rated flow. None of 26 bathroom exhaust systems tested exhausted at their manufacturers' rated flows, and most operated at 20 to 60 percent of their rated flows.

The following are the most common problems with residential exhaust systems:

◆ inadequate air flow and exhaust capability through installed fans and ductwork

◆ inadequate controls to allow for effective operation of the installed exhaust equipment

◆ home-owners' unwillingness to operate the equipment because of fan noise and discomfort resulting from drafts

◆ backdrafting and drafts resulting from the excessive capacity of exhaust appliances, creating negative pressures

5.2.1 INADEQUATE AIR FLOW

PROBLEM

INADEQUATE AIR FLOW

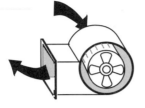

Axial flow fan (propeller)

Centrifugal blower (squirrel cage)

FIGURE 13
FAN TYPES

Room	Capacity L/s (cfm)
Master bedroom	10 (20)
Other bedrooms	5 (10)
Living room	5 (10)
Dining room	5 (10)
Family room	5 (10)
Recreation room	5 (10)
Basement	10 (20)
Other habitable rooms	5 (10)
Kitchen	5 (10)
Bathroom or	
Half bathroom	5 (10)
Laundry	5 (10)
Utility room	5 (10)

Table 1
Minimum Ventilation Requirements

CAUSE

Insufficient exhaust fan capacity

Many residential exhaust fans do not have sufficient capacity to exhaust the required amount of air. Two types of fans are commonly used in kitchen range hoods and bathroom exhaust fans: the axial flow (or propeller) type and the centrifugal (or squirrel-cage) type (see Figure 13).

Squirrel-cage fan designs are more expensive because of their more complicated blower wheel, but they are also more efficient, that is, they deliver more air flow against a higher pressure.

SOLUTIONS

◆ Size the total ventilation capacity of the home based on the minimum requirements listed in Table 1.

◆ Install a principal exhaust fan (or group of fans controlled simultaneously) which is rated to provide a minimum of 50 percent of the total ventilation capacity calculated using Table 1.

◆ Where bathrooms and kitchens are not serviced by the principal exhaust fan, bathroom fans should be capable of exhausting at a rate of 25 L/s (50 cfm) and kitchen-range hoods must have a rated capacity of not less than 50 L/s (100 cfm).

◆ Select exhaust fans with capacity and sound ratings determined in accordance with CSA C260, "Rating the Performance of Residential Mechanical Ventilating Equipment."

◆ Possible configurations for ventilation systems are illustrated in Figures 14 and 15 on the following page.

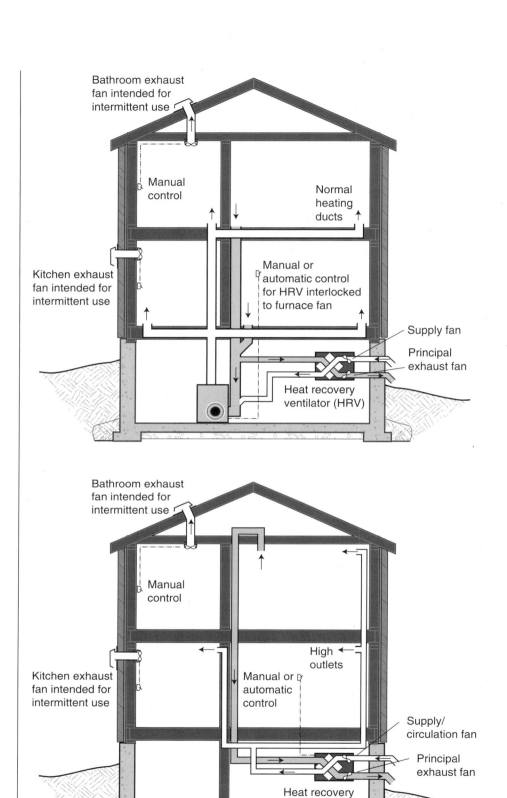

FIGURE 14
VENTILATION SYSTEMS COUPLED WITH FORCED-AIR HEATING SYSTEMS

FIGURE 15
VENTILATION SYSTEMS NOT COUPLED WITH FORCED-AIR HEATING SYSTEMS

PROBLEM
INADEQUATE AIR FLOW

CAUSE

Excessive air-flow resistance in the exhaust-fan ductwork

Resistance to air flow in poorly installed ductwork can restrict the ability of the fan to exhaust air.

SOLUTIONS

◆ Use a larger-diameter smooth sheet-metal duct. Avoid flexible ductwork.

◆ Minimize the number of bends in the duct run. The straighter the duct run, the greater the potential air flow.

◆ Size termination hoods properly.

CAUSE

Poor location of exhaust fans and exhaust air intake

Where exhaust fans and air intakes are not located in areas of high contaminant and pollution production, they may not provide adequate source relief.

SOLUTIONS

◆ Exhaust fans and air intakes in kitchens (other than range hoods or range top fans) should be located within 300 mm (12 in.) of the ceiling.

Do not locate range hoods more than 750 mm (30 in.) above the range surface. A recent study found that 450 mm (18 in.) is the best height at which the range hood captures cooking vapours without compromising access to the range top (see Figure 16).

◆ Exhaust fans and air intakes in bathrooms should be located close to the ceiling level to remove higher concentrations of moisture.

◆ When not located in bedrooms, exhaust air intakes should be capable of ensuring air flow from the bedrooms. Undercut doors, or provide a louvred panel to allow adequate air flow.

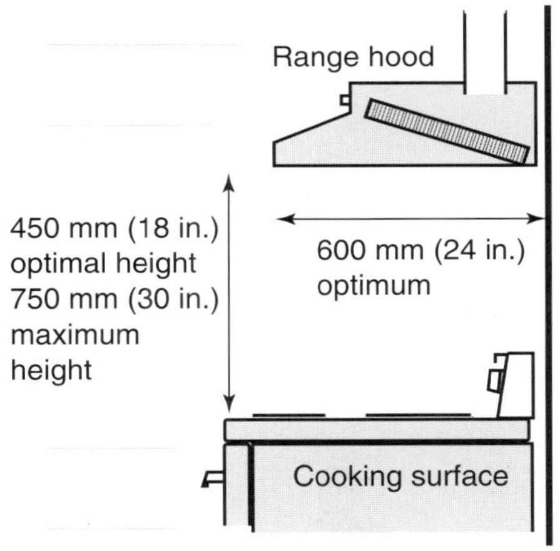

Range hood

450 mm (18 in.) optimal height
750 mm (30 in.) maximum height

600 mm (24 in.) optimum

Cooking surface

FIGURE 16
OPTIMUM DIMENSIONS FOR RANGE HOODS

PROBLEM
INADEQUATE AIR FLOW

CAUSE

Poor maintenance of exhaust system

Clogged filters and blocked ducting can reduce exhaust effectiveness.

SOLUTIONS

◆ Educate home-owners about the importance of properly maintaining exhaust fan filters and grilles.

◆ Ensure that grease filters in the kitchen exhaust equipment or air intakes are accessible and that home-owners are aware of the need to clean them regularly.

◆ Where a kitchen exhaust duct does not have an intake filter, the duct must be designed and installed so that the entire length of the duct can be cleaned.

◆ Ensure that home-owners are aware of the importance of regularly cleaning filters in heat-recovery ventilators (HRVs) and lint filters on dryers.

PROBLEM
INADEQUATE AIR FLOW AT PEAK PERIODS

CAUSE

Poorly designed and installed controls

SOLUTIONS

◆ Install an automated control system whose operation is based on indoor humidity levels. On continuous operation, the principal exhaust fan should be capable of ventilation at a minimum of 50 percent of the total ventilation capacity. Exhaust fans should be automatically capable of operating at higher levels.

◆ Educate home-owners about the importance of correctly setting dehumidistat controls to prevent the build-up of high levels of humidity and other contaminants in the home.

5.2.2 OPERATION OF EXHAUST EQUIPMENT
PROBLEM
HOME-OWNERS' UNWILLINGNESS TO OPERATE EXHAUST EQUIPMENT

CAUSE

Kitchen-range hood and bathroom fans run too noisily and are therefore not used by occupants.

SOLUTIONS

◆ The NBC requires that fans and range hoods be selected based on fan capacity and sound ratings determined in accordance with CSA C260, "Rating the Performance of Residential Mechanical Ventilating Equipment." Principal ventilation fans and bathroom fans should have a sound rating of not greater than 2.0 sones. Kitchen fans should have a sound rating of not greater than 3.5 sones.

◆ Ensure that the furnace circulating fan is properly installed to reduce vibration noises.

◆ Install a remotely mounted principal fan in the basement with vibration-isolating mounts. Consider the use of in-line fans.

◆ Fans should have a "soft" vibration-absorbing connection so as not to transfer vibration noise through the ducting.

CAUSE

Home-owners' perception that the operation of exhaust fans will increase energy costs

SOLUTIONS

◆ Install a heat-recovery ventilator (HRV) to recover heat from the exhaust air stream. HRVs can recover from 60 to 90 percent of the heat in the exhaust air stream, transferring the heat to the incoming fresh air stream.

◆ Inform home-owners about the health benefits resulting from the proper operation of exhaust air appliances.

CAUSE

The ventilation system is moving too much air, resulting in excessive dryness and low humidity levels.

SOLUTIONS

◆ Ensure that the dehumidistat is not set too low—meaning that high-speed operation of the principal exhaust system is seldom required. Reset to between 30 and 45 percent RH.

◆ If using a heat-recovery ventilator, ensure that the continuous ventilation rate complies with the manufacturer's recommendations. Reduce the continuous air flow rates if required.

◆ Ensure that intake and exhaust air flows are balanced within 10 percent of each other.

CAUSE

Humidifier not operating

In some cases, even when the house is ventilated at recommended levels, the house air will become too dry.

SOLUTIONS

◆ Ensure that the humidifier on the furnace operates correctly and only if the measured relative humidity is very low. Other steps should also be considered to increase humidity levels.

PROBLEM
BACKDRAFTING OF FUEL-FIRED APPLIANCES

CAUSE

House operating under a large negative pressure (for example, more than 5 Pa [0.000725 psi] of depressurization)

SOLUTIONS

◆ In houses that have fuel-fired appliances which are vented through a chimney, the NBC requires that where any individual exhaust device (or series of devices operated by a single switch) has a net ventilation capacity in excess of 75 L/s (150 cfm), make-up air must be provided to protect against depressurization. The supply fan for the make-up air should be wired so that it is activated when the exhaust device requiring the make-up air is operating.

◆ Make-up air entering the house must either be introduced into an unoccupied area of the house or tempered to at least 12°C (50°F) before being introduced into the supply-duct system or occupied areas of the house.

◆ Ensure that an outside combustion air supply, where required by the NBC, is provided for every combustion appliance.

PROBLEM
DISCOMFORT ASSOCIATED WITH DRAFTS AND COLD INCOMING AIR

CAUSE

House operating under negative pressure and drafts entering through ducting or through gaps in the building envelope

SOLUTIONS

◆ Temper the make-up air entering the house. One tempering option currently available for ventilation air is a heat-recovery ventilator. Other options include a CSA-approved fan and duct heater interlocked with the largest exhaust appliance in the house. The minimum output capacity of a duct heater or heating coil required by the NBC is determined using Table 2.

Required Minimum Capacity of Principal Exhaust Fan, L/s (cfm), as per Sentence 9.32.3.4.(1)	Minimum Output Capacity, kW				
	Outdoor Winter Design Temperature as per Article 2.2.1.1., °C (°F)				
	-15 (5) or above	-16 to -20 (3 to -4)	-21 to -25 (-6 to -13)	-26 to -30 (-15 to -22)	-31 (-24) or below
20 (40)	0.6	0.8	0.9	1.0	1.1
25 (50)	0.8	1.0	1.1	1.3	1.4
30 (60)	1.0	1.2	1.3	1.5	1.7
35 (70)	1.1	1.3	1.6	1.8	2.0
40 (80)	1.3	1.5	1.8	2.0	2.3
>40 (80)	Design to Subsection 9.33.4. (NBC)				

Table 2
Minimum Output Capacity of a Duct Heater

◆ Position supply air diffusers within 300 mm (12 in.) of the ceiling to promote diffusion of the cooler air across the ceiling.

Section 5.3 Educating Home-owners about Indoor Air Quality

Home-owners will benefit from your efforts to improve air quality only if they know how to operate and maintain ventilation equipment and combustion appliances. Your role as a builder is to teach home-owners the purpose of each device and the best methods to control and maintain them. If this is done properly, you will gain credibility, while transferring responsibility to the home-owners. Provide an owner's maintenance manual. High customer satisfaction and confidence often lead to future sales through word-of-mouth recommendations. Education also has the added benefit of reducing problems. Cover the following items:

Ventilation Systems

◆ Describe the ventilation system and its operation:
  - spot ventilation provided
  - rate of continuous ventilation
  - location of exhaust and supply intakes and outlets
  - location and operation of ventilation controls

◆ Make the home-owner aware of the need to do the following:
  - operate the ventilation system to control humidity levels in the home, reducing condensation on windows and minimizing potential moisture problems;
  - clean and replace filters regularly (provide additional filters or a list of suppliers); and
  - inspect and follow manufacturers' annual maintenance requirements for furnace fans and fans in HRVs.

◆ Show the home-owner the make-up air and tempering system. Explain the need for make-up air in preventing the house from operating under negative pressure and causing backdrafting of combustion appliances.

◆ Point out where HRV filters are located, and show how they are removed and cleaned. Inform home-owners of the need to clean HRV filters to maintain flow rates and flow balances.

◆ Explain that overventilation can lead to dryness in the house and high fuel consumption. Dehumidistats should be set at between 30 and 45 percent RH. In the coldest winter weather, the dehumidistat setting may need to be reduced to below 30 percent to avoid condensation and icing on windows.

◆ Advise home-owners not to tamper with balancing dampers.

◆ Describe the particular benefits of the ventilation system in the house.

Heating System

◆ Describe the type of heating system used in the house, and explain why it was chosen.

◆ If using sealed-draft or induced-draft natural gas appliances, describe the benefits of high efficiency and combustion safety.

◆ Explain the annual maintenance required.

Wood-Burning Appliances

◆ Demonstrate the safe operation of wood-burning appliances, and explain the benefits of proper operating practices (dry wood, controlled burn rates, etc.).

◆ Explain the importance of leaving the glass doors shut when the fireplace is left unattended and overnight.

◆ As applicable, explain the purpose and operation of the carbon monoxide detectors.

Gas Fireplaces

◆ Explain the general operation of a gas fireplace.

◆ Describe the benefits of a sealed-draft fireplace:

  – higher efficiency; and

  – elimination of flue-gas spillage.

◆ Describe the benefits of a fireplace with an outside combustion air kit:

  – higher efficiency because of the burning of outside air; and

  – spillage switch (show the home-owners how to reset it).

Some builders have home-buyers sign a waiver indicating that they have been informed about, and understand the importance of, the safe operation and maintenance of ventilation and heating equipment.

Section 5.4 Testing for Indoor Air Pollutants

Testing can be a very complicated and expensive task. Observation, common sense, and experience are often more appropriate guides. Tests also have limitations, and unless extensive tests are done, will generally not identify the sources of pollutants. However, testing can be useful for the following reasons:

◆ assessing whether the concentration of some of the more common pollutants is of concern

◆ determining the magnitude of the problem and confirming whether a major expense to improve indoor air quality is justified

◆ reassuring home-owners of the high indoor air quality in their house

◆ checking that the indoor air-quality measures taken by the builder are really effective

A wide range of methods are used in indoor air-quality testing. Most methods fall within three basic categories:

Time-averaged testing. This is a testing method that involves taking a continuous series of readings and averaging the results. This type of testing gives the average levels of a pollutant. Typical time-average testing includes the use of track-etch detectors for radon, and formaldehyde "badge" detectors.

Spot testing. This approach to testing is valuable for determining the peak levels of a household pollutant. The testing is usually performed when the house is operated in a way that produces the maximum pollutant levels; that is, when the ventilation system is shut off and the humidity and air temperatures are raised.

Continuous monitoring. In this method, a simple strip-chart recording device, such as a hygrothermograph for measuring temperature and humidity, can be used to monitor levels over a period of time.

In cases of callbacks where indoor air-quality problems are suspected, individuals who have completed an accredited course (i.e., CMHC's Indoor Air Quality Investigator's Course) can be called upon to assist in identifying the problems. A list of these individuals can be obtained from CMHC offices.

Section 5.5 Additional Reading

SOURCE	PUBLICATION
Canada Mortgage and Housing Corporation Canadian Housing Information Centre 700 Montreal Road Ottawa ON K1A 0P7 613 748-2367	*This Clean House* video, 1995 *Complying with Ventilation Requirements of the 1995 NBC,* 1995 *Building Materials for the Environmentally Hypersensitive,* 1994 *The Clean Air Guide,* 1993 *Clean-up Procedures for Mold in Houses,* 1991 *Housing for the Environmentally Hypersensitive,* 1990
Ontario New Home Warranty Program 5160 Yonge Street, 6th Floor North York ON M2N 6L9 416 229-9200	*Complying with Ventilation Requirements of the 1993 OBC,* 1993 *Your New Home's Ventilation System,* 1994

APPENDIX A SOURCES OF INFORMATION

- ◆ Health Canada
- ◆ CMHC research personnel located at the Corporation's National Office in Ottawa
- ◆ Canadian Centre for Occupational Health and Safety
- ◆ The Canadian Lung Association

Understanding Health Canada Guidelines

Health Canada, in conjunction with the provinces, has developed a set of guidelines for exposure to indoor air pollutants in housing. These guidelines are for both short-term exposure (acceptable short-term exposure range, or ASTER) and long-term exposure (acceptable long-term exposure range, or ALTER). ASTER guidelines are for a specified period of time, typically one to 24 hours. ALTER guidelines are considered safe for continuous exposure over a lifetime. See Table 3 for ALTER and ASTER guidelines for common indoor air pollutants.

Pollutant	Acceptable Long-Term Exposure (ALTER)	Acceptable Short-Term Exposure (ASTER)
Formaldehyde*	0.05 ppm (parts per million)	Less than 0.1 ppm (parts per million)
Carbon Dioxide	3 500 ppm	Less than 7 000 ppm
Carbon Monoxide	None	Less than 11 ppm averaged over 8 hours Less than 25 ppm 1-hour average
Nitrogen Dioxide	Less than .052 ppm	Less than 0.25 ppm 1-hour average
Moisture (Water Vapour)	30% to 80% relative humidity in the summer 30% to 45% relative humidity in the winter	100%
Sulphur Dioxide	Less than 0.019 ppm	Less than 0.38 ppm 5-minute average

* For formaldehyde, the guidelines specify a long-term "target level" rather than an ALTER, and a short-term "action level" rather than an ASTER.

Table 3
Health and Welfare Guidelines for Exposure to Indoor Air Pollutants in Housing

APPENDIX B   POLLUTANTS

Pollutant	Sources in the Home	Health Effects	Methods of Pollutant Control
Formaldehyde Colourless gas with strong odour	Various construction materials, including particleboard, interior panelling, and drapes	Eye, nose, and throat irritation	Substitute oriented strandboard (OSB) and exterior-grade plywoods for particleboards. Seal particleboards with low-toxicity vapour-proof sealers, and paint or varnish in cabinets and closets and on subflooring. Increase ventilation rates.
Radon Odourless, colourless radioactive gas	Soil beneath and around the house foundation	Believed to be the cause of 5 to 10 percent of all lung cancer	Seal floor drains, sumps, and all cracks, joints, and penetrations through basement walls and slab. Ventilate crawl space tightly, and seal subfloor joints and penetrations. Depressurize the gravel bed beneath slab or isolate the basement from the rest of the house, and pressurize it with air drawn from the floors above.
Carbon Monoxide Colourless, odourless gas	Kerosene heaters, wood-burning appliances, unvented gas appliances, attached garages, blocked chimneys, and malfunctioning furnaces	Nausea, headaches, and blue fingernails. Severe poisoning can cause brain damage in fetuses and can be fatal	Provide outside combustion air feed to the firebox of all wood-burning appliances. Install tight-fitting doors on fireplaces and wood stoves. Vent gas ranges directly to the outside. Provide adequately sized, tempered make-up air for exhaust fans. Use induced-draft or sealed-draft hot water heaters and furnaces.

Pollutant	Sources in the Home	Health Effects	Methods of Pollutant Control
Nitrogen Dioxide Has odour when present in large quantities	Kerosene heaters and unvented gas appliances	Lung damage and increased potential for lung disease after long exposure	Same as above
Respirable Suspended Particulates Particles suspended in the air that can be inhaled	Tobacco smoke, wood smoke, unvented gas appliances, kerosene heaters, asbestos construction materials, dust	Eye, nose, and throat irritation, lung cancer, emphysema, heart disease, bronchitis, respiratory infections	Avoid smoking inside. Ensure wood-burning appliances and flues do not leak. Vent combustion appliances outside. Provide outside combustion air feed to the fireboxes of all wood-burning appliances. Install tight-fitting doors on fireplaces and wood stoves. Increase ventilation rates. Use medium efficiency pleated fabric filters or HEPA filters in the furnace and change them regularly.
Moisture High humidity	Ground water entering through the foundation, cleaning, bathing, washing, and respiration	Causes growth of micro-organisms, increases release of formaldehyde.	Place a drainage pad of crushed stone beneath the foundation, and provide drainage at the foundation's perimeter. Seal beneath the foundation with a polyethylene barrier. Provide adequate ventilation. Vent dryer directly to the outside.
Organic Solvents	Household cleaners and solvents in paints and caulkings	Eye, nose, and throat irritation, can affect central nervous system	Use solvent-based materials in well-ventilated areas. Substitute water-based paints and caulking for solvent-based products.

Table 4
Summary of Common Indoor Air Pollutants, their Health Effects, Sources, and Some Methods of Control

CHAPTER 6
Introduction

NOISE CONTROL

Noise—whether it originates inside or out—is an unwelcome intruder in any home. It devalues privacy and indeed the worth of the building itself. Unwanted sound has many sources: noisy plumbing and neighbours' stereos are two examples.

Materials used in construction help reduce noise in two distinct ways: they can absorb sound waves or they can act as barriers against their transmission. Sound-absorbing materials, such as carpets and acoustic ceiling tiles, can effectively muffle noise generated in a room. To reduce noise transmission between rooms or storeys, sound-absorbing materials in the cavity of the barrier walls or floors will do the best job. The common thermal insulations (cellulose fibre, mineral fibre, and some open-cell foams) are good sound absorbers for barrier cavities, while closed-cell foams such as polystyrene and polyurethane generally are not.

Drywall, plywood, concrete, and glass are good sound barriers.

The decibel is the standard measure of loudness. The Sound Transmission Class (STC) indicates the average noise reduction in decibels for sounds passing through walls or floors. The higher the STC, the greater the noise reduction. For example, an STC 60 wall would let 10 times less sound through than an STC 50 wall. The ear would perceive this as half the sound coming through, so the STC 60 wall is perceived as being twice as good as the STC 50 wall.

Floors receive a similar rating, called the Impact Insulation Class (IIC).

The *National Building Code* requires a minimum STC of 50 for common walls and floors. Builders should provide STC 55 to ensure good acoustic privacy. Where exceptional sound isolation is desired, STC 60 is a more appropriate goal. Table 1 gives both the required and some suggested minimum STC and IIC values.

Structural Element	NBC Req. STC	Suggested Minimum STC	Suggested Minimum IIC
Party walls or floors	50	55	—
Bare party floors	50	55	55
Carpeted party floors	50	55	65
Elevator shafts	55	60	—

Table 1
Required and Suggested Minimum STC and IIC for Occupant Satisfaction for Various Structural Elements

This guide is an introduction to noise control. It deals mainly with common lightweight or porous constructions—wood- or steel-frame, or concrete-block—since these can easily provide very good noise control but are also easily spoiled by small oversights or errors. Additional information can be found in other CMHC publications listed at the end of this chapter.

6.1 Walls, Floors, and Ceilings
PROBLEM
NOISE INTRUSION FROM AN ADJOINING APARTMENT

CAUSE

A deficiency in the party wall

SOLUTIONS

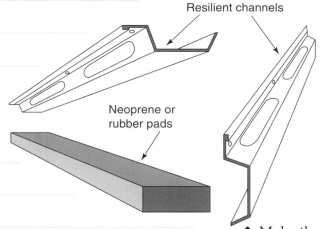

Resilient channels

Neoprene or rubber pads

FIGURE 1
RESILIENT CONNECTIONS

◆ Build the wall as two or more separate layers. The heavier the layers, the better the noise reduction. Very dense materials, such as steel or lead, give weight with minimum thickness. Such unusual materials are used in a wall only if the sound barrier must be kept thin.

◆ Eliminate solid contact between the layers. Where connections are needed, they must be resilient. An air space, resilient metal furring, rubber, steel springs, or cushioning blankets are used to reduce vibration transmission between one side or layer of a wall or floor and the next (see Figure 1).

◆ Make the cavity as deep as practical. A thin air space can transmit too much vibration from layer to layer.

◆ Reduce party-wall leaks through back-to-back electrical outlets by offsetting them at least 400 mm (16 in.), and be sure fibrous insulation fills in behind them so that leaks do not lead directly to the air space. Sealed air-vapour-barrier electrical boxes designed for exterior walls are ideal for sound-barrier walls.

◆ Call in an acoustical consultant for STC testing and advice..

PROBLEM

KITCHEN, BATHROOM, AND ENTERTAINMENT NOISES ARE CLEARLY AUDIBLE IN THE "QUIET" AREAS OF A NEIGHBOURING APARTMENT

CAUSE

Poor layout: noisy rooms in one apartment are beside quiet rooms next door.

SOLUTIONS

◆ Install rubber or felt bumpers to cushion the impact of slamming kitchen cupboard doors and drawers .

◆ Check for obvious leaks or flanking paths. "Flanking" refers to transmission around a barrier: sound is conducted by structural materials or cavities that bypass the barrier intended to separate rooms or spaces. Such alternative paths increase the amount of sound transmission in buildings, even if there is good design and construction. For example, running a plywood subfloor under a costly double-stud party wall can reduce sound blockage from outstanding to unacceptable.

◆ Have the designer plan apartments that place rooms with similar noise levels against both sides of the party wall.

PROBLEM

INSUFFICIENT NOISE REDUCTION, EVEN THOUGH THE WOOD-STUD WALL CONTAINS SOUND-ABSORBING MATERIAL

CAUSE

Drywall directly attached to the wood studs on both sides

SOLUTIONS

◆ Remove the drywall from one side of the wall. Then, install an independent row of studs, put more sound-absorbing material in the new deeper cavity, and attach drywall to the new studs.

◆ Remove the drywall from one side. Ensure that the sound-absorbing insulation fills the cavity to at least three quarters of its thickness. Common fibrous insulations—about R12 or STC 50 in thermal terms—are ideal. Attach resilient metal furring to studs, attach drywall to the furring, and seal the bottom of the drywall with permanent acoustic sealant.

CAUSE

Unknown design or construction error. Existing wall cannot be disturbed.

SOLUTIONS

◆ Install an independent row of studs. Put sound-absorbing material in the new cavity, and attach two layers of drywall to the new studs (see Figure 2a). The farther the additional layers of drywall are from the existing wall the better the reduction of low-frequency noise; a thin air space can transmit much vibration from layer to layer.

◆ Attach strapping to the existing wall. (Use a combination of wood strapping and resilient metal furring, or steel studs only.) Put sound-absorbing material in the cavity, and attach two layers of drywall to the new assembly (see Figure 2b).

Existing wall

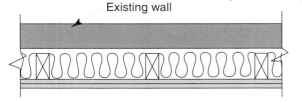

Existing wall

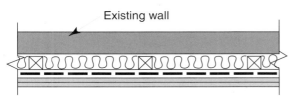

FIGURE 2
ADDITIONAL DRYWALL SUPPORTS

PROBLEM

MOUNTING DRYWALL ON RESILIENT METAL FURRING DOES NOT SUFFICIENTLY REDUCE NOISE TRANSMISSION.

CAUSE

Drywall screws that are too long, "short-circuiting" the resilient metal furring

SOLUTIONS

◆ Remove all screws that are too long and replace with shorter ones. Repair the wall. The greater the number of screws that contact the studs or joists, the poorer the noise reduction will be.

CAUSE

Resilient metal furring between two layers of drywall (forming a small air space) with a solid connection of the inner layer to the studs

SOLUTIONS

◆ Do not mount two layers of drywall, or any other solid sheet material, so that there is a thin air space between them; it fails to act as a fully resilient separator. Place the resilient metal furring directly on the studs or joists to avoid rattling, and then apply the drywall (see Figure 3). Twenty-four gauge or thinner steel studs are resilient enough in themselves, so that no special measures are needed to isolate the layers of the wall from each other.

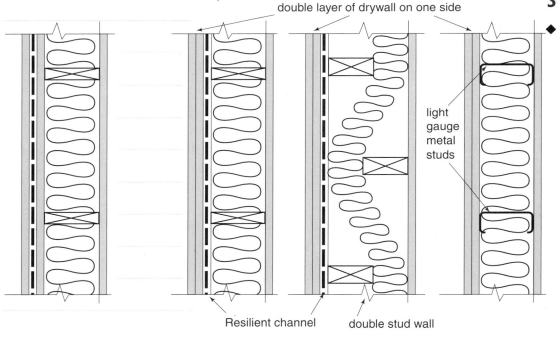

double layer of drywall on one side

light gauge metal studs

Resilient channel   double stud wall

Incorrect   Correct

FIGURE 3
RESILIENT METAL FURRING AND DRYWALL PLACEMENT

PROBLEM

SOUND LEAKING CLOSE TO THE FLOOR-WALL JUNCTION

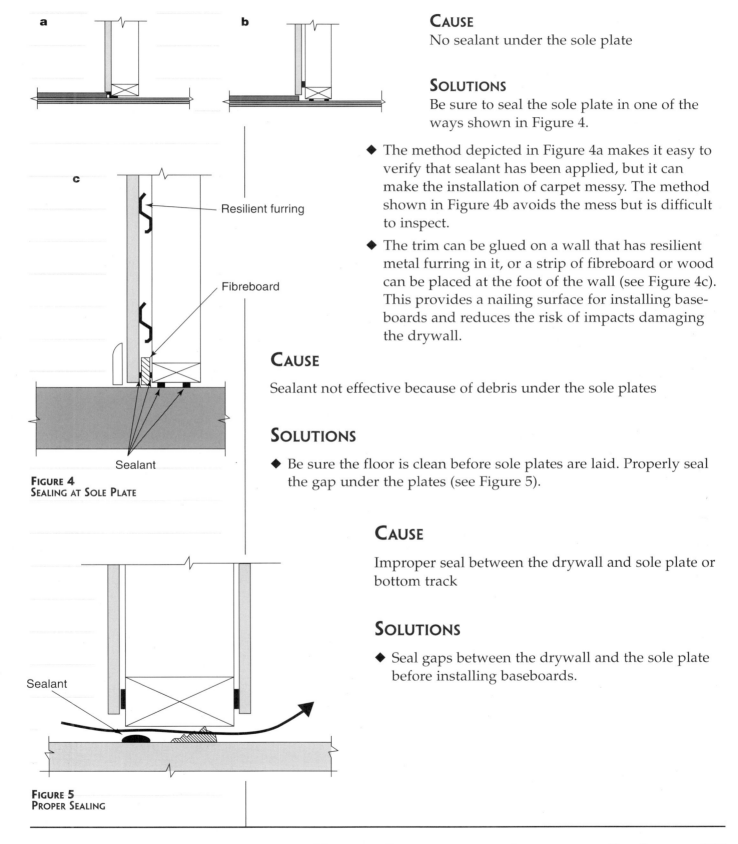

a

b

c

Resilient furring

Fibreboard

Sealant

FIGURE 4
SEALING AT SOLE PLATE

Sealant

FIGURE 5
PROPER SEALING

CAUSE

No sealant under the sole plate

SOLUTIONS

Be sure to seal the sole plate in one of the ways shown in Figure 4.

◆ The method depicted in Figure 4a makes it easy to verify that sealant has been applied, but it can make the installation of carpet messy. The method shown in Figure 4b avoids the mess but is difficult to inspect.

◆ The trim can be glued on a wall that has resilient metal furring in it, or a strip of fibreboard or wood can be placed at the foot of the wall (see Figure 4c). This provides a nailing surface for installing baseboards and reduces the risk of impacts damaging the drywall.

CAUSE

Sealant not effective because of debris under the sole plates

SOLUTIONS

◆ Be sure the floor is clean before sole plates are laid. Properly seal the gap under the plates (see Figure 5).

CAUSE

Improper seal between the drywall and sole plate or bottom track

SOLUTIONS

◆ Seal gaps between the drywall and the sole plate before installing baseboards.

PROBLEM

SOUND LEAKING THROUGH ELECTRICAL OUTLETS

CAUSE

Unsealed, back-to-back electrical outlets

SOLUTIONS

◆ Offset outlets from each other along the wall at least 400 mm (16 in.) as shown in Figure 6. Keep holes as small as possible. Seal the openings with acoustic sealant. Insulate the cavity, including behind the outlets.

◆ In existing housing, seal the outlets as much as possible if they have already been installed, or use foam gaskets. If necessary, open up and block off with dense insulation and sealed blocking.

◆ Extend internal blocking to guard against leaks around electrical outlets and at the foot of a double-stud wall.

◆ Use sound-absorbing materials inside walls and floors. The structure can be designed so that leaking sound must travel through much sound-absorbing material.

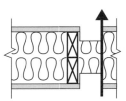

Unsealed back-to-back outlets

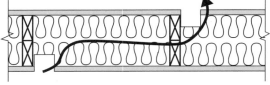

Offset outlets

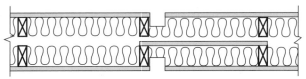

Use sound-absorbing materials

FIGURE 6
ELECTRICAL OUTLETS

PROBLEM

CONCRETE BLOCK WALL NOT PROVIDING SUFFICIENT NOISE REDUCTION

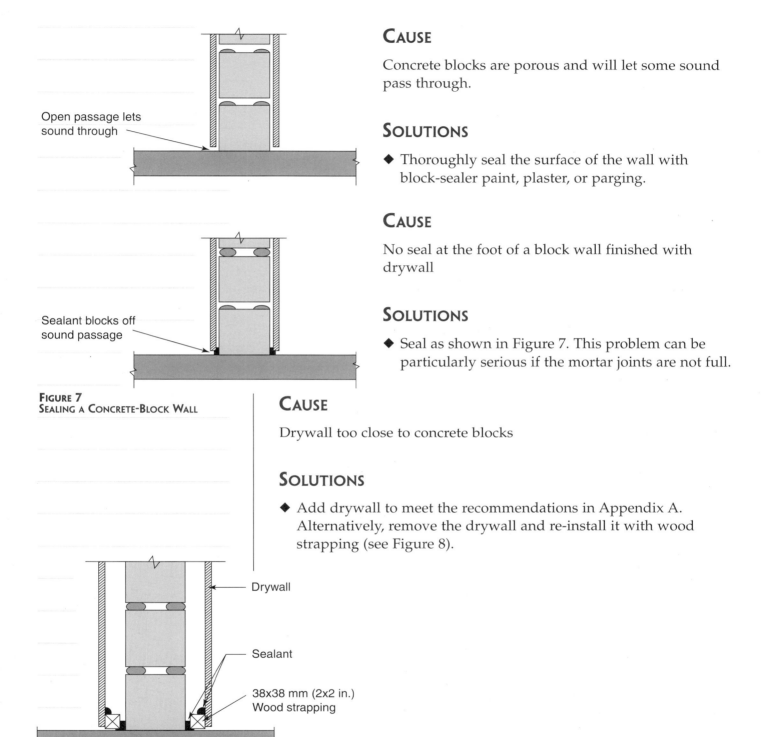

Open passage lets sound through

Sealant blocks off sound passage

FIGURE 7
SEALING A CONCRETE-BLOCK WALL

Drywall

Sealant

38x38 mm (2x2 in.) Wood strapping

FIGURE 8
DRYWALL ON A CONCRETE-BLOCK WALL

CAUSE

Concrete blocks are porous and will let some sound pass through.

SOLUTIONS

◆ Thoroughly seal the surface of the wall with block-sealer paint, plaster, or parging.

CAUSE

No seal at the foot of a block wall finished with drywall

SOLUTIONS

◆ Seal as shown in Figure 7. This problem can be particularly serious if the mortar joints are not full.

CAUSE

Drywall too close to concrete blocks

SOLUTIONS

◆ Add drywall to meet the recommendations in Appendix A. Alternatively, remove the drywall and re-install it with wood strapping (see Figure 8).

Do not paint, plaster, or parge the blocks under the drywall. The untreated porous blocks will help increase the effective air space of the cavity.

Construct the following minimum air spaces between the drywall and the blocks:

Drywall Thickness	1 sheet	2 sheets (same side)
12.7 mm (1/2 in.)	60 mm (2-3/8 in.)	30 mm (1-3/16 in.)
15.9 mm (5/8 in.)	47 mm (1-7/8 in.)	25 mm (1 in.)

Choose from the methods of resilient attachment illustrated in Figure 9.

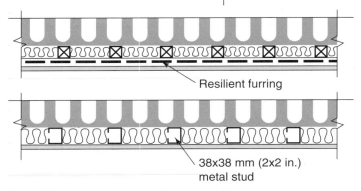

Resilient furring

38x38 mm (2x2 in.) metal stud

FIGURE 9
RESILIENT ATTACHMENT TO CONCRETE BLOCKS

PROBLEM
POURED-CONCRETE WALL DOES NOT PROVIDE ADEQUATE NOISE REDUCTION

CAUSE

Holes or honeycomb penetrations in the structure

SOLUTIONS

◆ Seal all obvious fissures or holes with grout or plaster before finishing the wall.

CAUSE

Holes or honeycomb penetrations in the structure and no seal at the foot of the drywall

SOLUTIONS

◆ Seal all obvious fissures or holes with grout or plaster before finishing the wall. Seal the gap at the bottom of the drywall for extra security (see Figure 10).

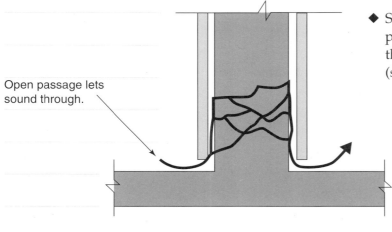

Open passage lets sound through.

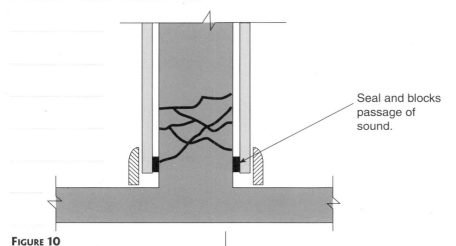

Seal and blocks passage of sound.

FIGURE 10
SEALING POURED-CONCRETE WALL

PROBLEM
POOR NOISE REDUCTION FROM A LIGHTWEIGHT FLOOR SYSTEM (AIRBORNE NOISE)

CAUSE

Ceiling directly attached to the floor joists

SOLUTIONS

Use resilient metal furring to support the ceiling (see Appendix B).

◆ Do not use nailed wood furrings, since the rigid coupling they provide between the floor and the ceiling transmits sound vibrations through them.

◆ Double the mass of a drywall ceiling installed on resilient furrings to reduce noise transmission. Do not do the same on nailed wood furrings; it does not improve noise control.

CAUSE

Poor sealing at edges of ceiling

SOLUTIONS

◆ Seal the wall-ceiling junction with regular tape and joint compound.

PROBLEM

FLOOR WITH ACOUSTIC CEILING NOT PROVIDING ENOUGH NOISE REDUCTION FROM STOREY ABOVE

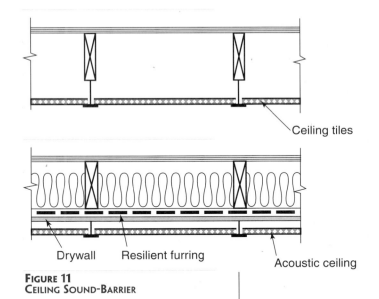

Ceiling tiles

Drywall   Resilient furring

Acoustic ceiling

FIGURE 11
CEILING SOUND-BARRIER

CAUSE

No effective sound barrier in ceiling

SOLUTIONS

◆ Remove the acoustic ceiling. Install sound-absorbing fibrous insulation to three-quarters the depth in the cavity, and apply drywall on resilient metal furring. Re-install the acoustic ceiling if desired to reduce the echo in the room (see Figure 11).

PROBLEM

FLOOR NOT PROVIDING ENOUGH INSULATION FROM IMPACT SOUND

CAUSE

Upper layer not heavy enough, or no direct absorbing of impacts

SOLUTIONS

◆ Add carpet on underpad.

◆ Increase the weight of the upper layer of the floor to at least 50 kg/m² (10 lb/sq. ft.) by adding a concrete layer or equivalent. Install underpad and carpet.

◆ Install a floating floor as shown in Figure 12. A carpet on top of the floating floor will give additional protection but may not be needed.

◆ Build an additional ceiling under the existing one. A ceiling of 12-mm (1/2-in.) drywall, fastened to 64-mm (3-in.) standard metal studs (which act as resilient furring) with batt insulation between the studs, provides good results.

◆ Use heavy layers, such as concrete, lightweight concrete, gypsum concrete, or gypsum board over the plywood subfloor.

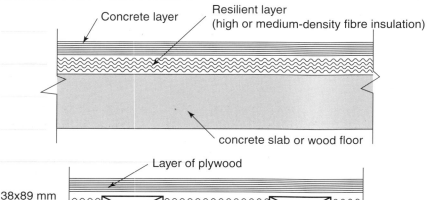

Concrete layer

Resilient layer (high or medium-density fibre insulation)

concrete slab or wood floor

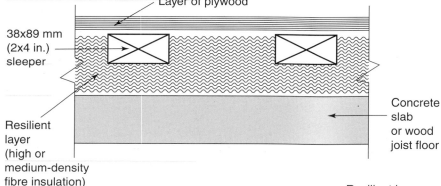

Layer of plywood

38x89 mm (2x4 in.) sleeper

Resilient layer (high or medium-density fibre insulation)

Concrete slab or wood joist floor

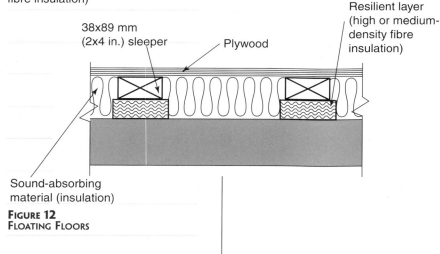

Resilient layer (high or medium-density fibre insulation)

38x89 mm (2x4 in.) sleeper

Plywood

Sound-absorbing material (insulation)

FIGURE 12
FLOATING FLOORS

PROBLEM
FLOATING FLOOR NOT PROVIDING EXPECTED NOISE REDUCTION

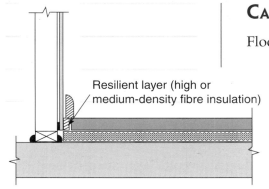

Resilient layer (high or medium-density fibre insulation)

FIGURE 13
FLOATING FLOOR DISTANCE FROM EDGES

CAUSE

Floor contacting structure at edges

SOLUTIONS

◆ Stop the floating floor from touching the walls at the edges, as shown in Figure 13.

CAUSE

Nails or screws penetrating the resilient layer to contact the subfloor or joists

SOLUTIONS

◆ Remove all nails or screws that are too long. Design the floor so that the top layer can truly "float" and does not need to be nailed to the subfloor.

CAUSE

Concrete lumps or debris under the floating slab compress the resilient layer so much that it becomes hard and transmits sound.

SOLUTIONS

◆ Be sure that the subfloor is level and free of debris before laying the resilient blanket.

Section 6.2 Flanking Sound

PROBLEM

GOOD WALL DESIGN BUT POOR NOISE REDUCTION

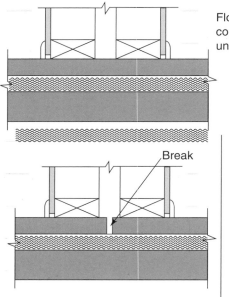

Floor rigidly
connected
under wall

Break

FIGURE 14
CONCRETE FLOOR

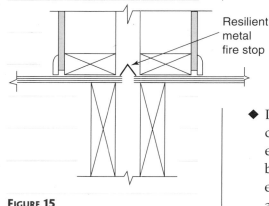

Resilient
metal
fire stop

FIGURE 15
WOOD FLOOR

CAUSE

Flanking transmission along the top layer of a concrete floor

SOLUTIONS

◆ Avoid installing floor systems that are rigidly connected under a lightweight wall. Flanking sound can travel along the top layer or in the joist to radiate in the room on the other side. Eliminate by introducing a break in the structure (see Figure 14). Use this type of floor construction with heavy walls only.

CAUSE

Flanking transmission along the top layer of a wood floor

SOLUTIONS

◆ Do not allow continuous layers of wood to pass under the wall. Make a saw-cut to prevent this happening with double stud systems. Do not use continuous joists under a party wall. Use a resilient metal fire-stop, not gypsum board, to ensure effective separation as shown in Figure 15.

◆ Do not include a continuous subfloor, or one that is effectively continuous because of gypsum-board firestopping: it can make an excellent STC 62 party wall behave like an inadequate STC 45 barrier. The subfloor may act as a structural diaphragm, and an engineer will have to assess it before you will be able to reach it and saw it. Adding a true floating floor on each side may be the only way to improve the situation.

CAUSE

Transmission through the floor into the common cavity underneath

SOLUTIONS

◆ Block all openings above and below the party wall.

CAUSE

Flanking transmission through the attic space

SOLUTIONS

◆ Extend the party wall to the roof (see Figure 16).

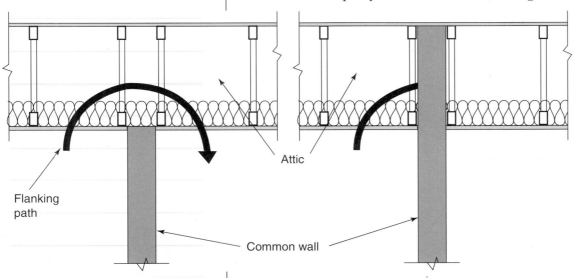

Attic

Flanking path

Common wall

FIGURE 16
ATTIC SPACE

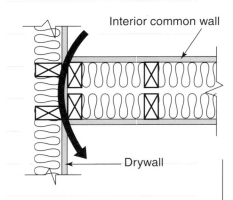

FIGURE 17
DRYWALL AT PARTY FLOORS AND WALLS

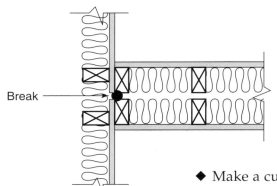

CAUSE

Flanking transmissions along single continuous layers of drywall on walls at right angles to the party wall or floor

SOLUTIONS

◆ Make a cut in the drywall to prevent flanking transmission. Put acoustic sealant in the cut to provide an air seal on an outside wall (see Figure 17)

PROBLEM

EXCESSIVE NOISE TRANSMISSION THROUGH THE FLOOR, ESPECIALLY FOOTSTEP AND IMPACT SOUND

CAUSE

Flanking transmission down the walls

SOLUTIONS

Install a floating floor.

◆ Attach drywall to ceilings and both sides of walls using resilient metal furring. This reduces flanking sound travelling down the walls to the room below (see Figure 18).

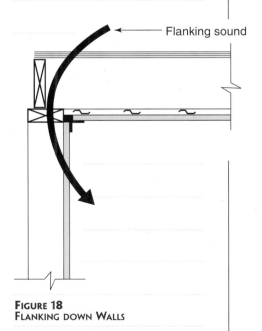

FIGURE 18
FLANKING DOWN WALLS

Flanking sound

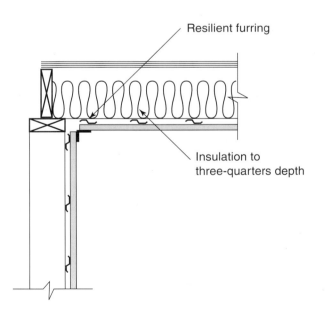

Resilient furring

Insulation to three-quarters depth

PROBLEM
SOUND BEING TRANSMITTED THROUGH HOLLOW-CORE PRECAST CONCRETE SLABS

CAUSE

The joint between slabs not well sealed

SOLUTIONS

◆ Seal the joint with grout if the gap between the precast slabs is large. Fill the joint with a polypropylene rope, and seal it with acoustic sealant.

CAUSE

Sound travels through the cores from the corridors of other apartments

SOLUTIONS

◆ Isolate the apartment from the slab by installing a floating floor.

PROBLEM
EXCESSIVE NOISE TRANSMISSION BETWEEN BATHROOMS

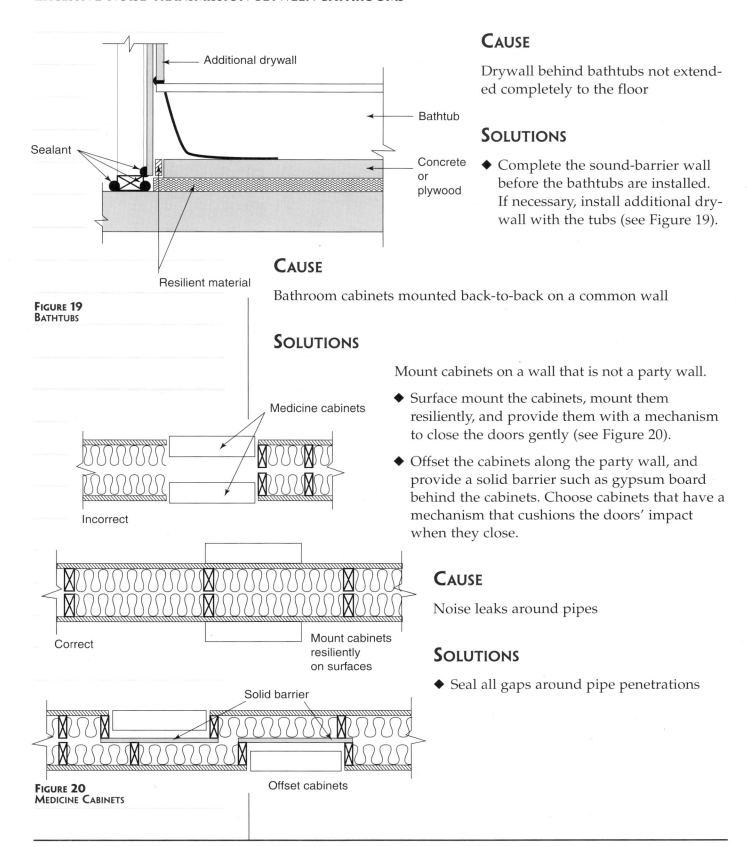

Additional drywall

Sealant

Bathtub

Concrete
or
plywood

Resilient material

FIGURE 19
BATHTUBS

Medicine cabinets

Incorrect

Correct

Mount cabinets
resiliently
on surfaces

Solid barrier

Offset cabinets

FIGURE 20
MEDICINE CABINETS

CAUSE

Drywall behind bathtubs not extended completely to the floor

SOLUTIONS

◆ Complete the sound-barrier wall before the bathtubs are installed. If necessary, install additional drywall with the tubs (see Figure 19).

CAUSE

Bathroom cabinets mounted back-to-back on a common wall

SOLUTIONS

Mount cabinets on a wall that is not a party wall.

◆ Surface mount the cabinets, mount them resiliently, and provide them with a mechanism to close the doors gently (see Figure 20).

◆ Offset the cabinets along the party wall, and provide a solid barrier such as gypsum board behind the cabinets. Choose cabinets that have a mechanism that cushions the doors' impact when they close.

CAUSE

Noise leaks around pipes

SOLUTIONS

◆ Seal all gaps around pipe penetrations

PROBLEM
FOOTSTEPS ON STAIRS CLEARLY AUDIBLE IN NEIGHBOURING APARTMENTS

CAUSE

Stairs attached to a party wall

SOLUTIONS

◆ Support the stairs on a wall other than the party wall.

◆ Design units so that the stairs are not close to the common wall.

◆ Use good quality carpet and underpad on the stairs.

◆ In stairwells, support the stairs on structural elements that are separate from the building structure.

Section 6.3 Plumbing Noise
PROBLEM
PLUMBING NOISE HEARD ALL OVER THE APARTMENT AND IN THE NEIGHBOURING APARTMENT

CAUSE

Pipes rigidly connected to walls

SOLUTIONS

◆ To avoid vibration, isolate the pipe system with resilient sleeves and hangers. Avoid all rigid contact with the building structure (see Figure 21).

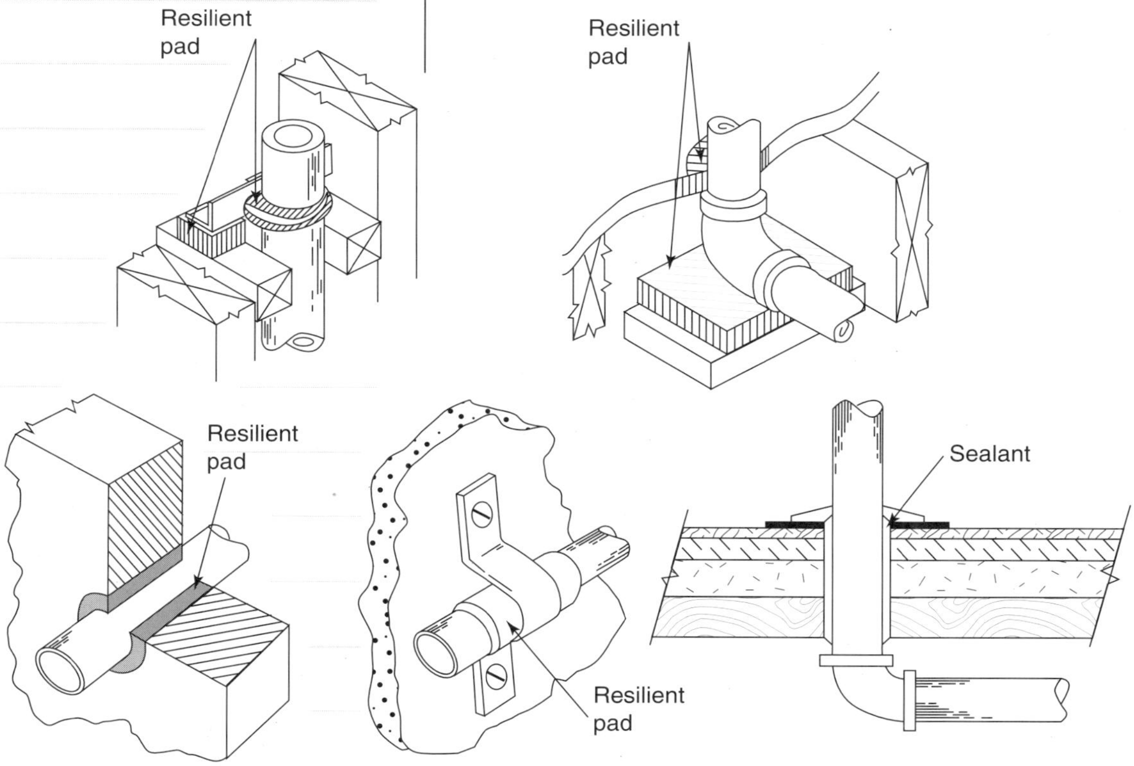

FIGURE 21
PIPES

Cause

Turbulence caused by high water-pressure and an excessive number of elbows and bends

Solutions

◆ Minimize the number of fittings and bends.

◆ Use large-diameter piping for all main supply lines. Limit water speed to less than 2 m (6-1/2 ft.) per second by using a pressure reduction valve.

Cause

Turbulence from noisy valves and fixtures

Solutions

◆ Install quiet valves and fixtures. Some valves are reasonably quiet when full on but are noisy when half on. Check with the manufacturer.

PROBLEM

BATH, SHOWER, AND TOILET NOISES HEARD IN NEIGHBOURING APARTMENTS

CAUSE

Waste pipes installed close to quiet areas

SOLUTIONS

◆ Install waste pipes away from quiet areas, and do not let them contact the building structure directly. Enclose them in separate pipe chases with extra noise reduction material if necessary.

CAUSE

Bathtub, shower, or toilet rigidly attached to the building structure

SOLUTIONS

◆ Use rubber, neoprene, or other resilient pads to reduce vibration transmitted into the structure (see Figure 22).

CAUSE

A noisy toilet solidly connected to the floor

SOLUTIONS

◆ Install siphon-jet toilets. They are much quieter than conventional units.

◆ Install toilets on resilient bases.

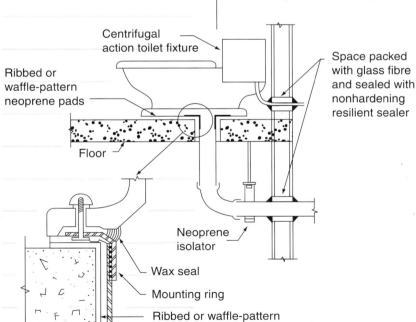

Centrifugal action toilet fixture

Space packed with glass fibre and sealed with nonhardening resilient sealer

Ribbed or waffle-pattern neoprene pads

Floor

Neoprene isolator

Wax seal

Mounting ring

Ribbed or waffle-pattern neoprene pads (2 layers)

FIGURE 22
TUBS, TOILETS AND SHOWERS

PROBLEM

LOUD BANGING WHEN DISHWASHER AND CLOTHES WASHING MACHINE VALVES OPERATE.

CAUSE

Water hammer-shock waves generated when valves close too rapidly

SOLUTIONS

◆ Install air cushions or mechanical bumpers right next to appliances, such as washing machines and dishwashers, equipped with fast-acting valves (see Figure 23).

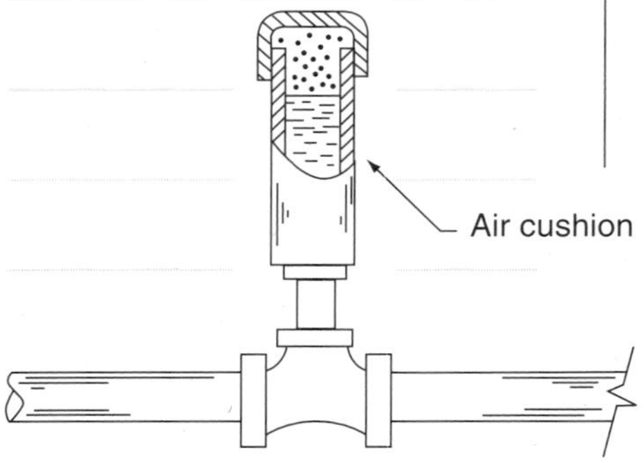

Air cushion

FIGURE 23
VALVES

Section 6.4 External Noise

PROBLEM

OUTDOOR NOISE PENETRATION INTO THE HOME

CAUSE

Windows left open to provide ventilation. At noisy sites, windows must be closed for acceptable noise reduction.

SOLUTIONS

Install a suitable ventilation system so that windows can normally be left closed.

◆ Use a forced-air ventilation system with noise-control features.

◆ Put the inlet for outdoor air and the exhaust outlet in the quietest locations possible.

◆ Control noise entering through the inlet and outlet ducts by putting an acoustic duct liner inside the ducts. Acoustic duct liners have rigid glass fibre lined with a cloth coating and are glued to the inside of the ducts.

Air conditioning can easily be included in such a system for greater summer comfort.

CAUSE

Noise leaks around windows or doors

SOLUTIONS

◆ Adjust or replace weatherstripping. Test weatherstripping by temporarily sealing the door or window with duct tape at all edges. If there is an audible change, fix the weatherstripping. Even new weatherstripping may be badly installed or unsuitable for noise control.

◆ Install only one window that opens in a group of windows. This will reduce noise transmitted through leaks.

◆ Ensure that there is airtight detailing around the glazing and the sash. Airtight packing or urethane foam between window frames and rough openings can control noise penetration as well, as can interior caulking of the window trim joints to the wall and the window.

Cause

Noise transmitted through an inadequate window

Solutions

In general, for good noise reduction, avoid large areas of window in locations where high noise levels exist, and

◆ use thick glass (6 mm [1/4 in.]), or laminated glass if thicker;

◆ use as large an air space between the glass layers as possible with the available frames. For very noisy sites, an air space of 50 to 100 mm (2 to 4 in.) is desirable; this is not possible with typical factory-sealed glazing; or

◆ use triple glazing for severe cases.

Add a storm window:

◆ Add a storm window with as large an air space between the storm and the inner windows as the frame permits.

◆ Install very good weatherstripping on the inner window. To avoid condensation on the storm window, do not seal it tightly.

Cause

Noise transmitted through an inadequate door

Solutions

Change the floor plan to include a vestibule.

◆ If extremely good noise reduction is needed, use a sound-lock vestibule rather than a storm door. Remember that windows in the vestibule usually increase noise transmission.

◆ Install the inner door with the smallest possible clearance at all edges.

In most cases, a hollow-core wood door is adequate. A pocket door may be more convenient for some floor plans.

Add a storm door.

◆ Install the storm door so that the space between the doors is as large as possible.

◆ Install good weatherstripping on both doors. The thickness and thermal insulation performance of the storm door are not important for noise control.

Use a good quality door.

◆ Do not replace a solid-core wood door with a metal door to improve noise control; the improvement is very slight.

◆ Window panels in a door do not significantly change noise levels.

Cause

Noise transmitted through an exterior wall

Solutions

Use a heavy exterior surface. Brick veneer or concrete block provide more noise reduction than vinyl, light metal or wood facing.

◆ Reduce stiff connections between the inner and outer surfaces of the wall by mounting interior drywall on resilient metal furring or using double-stud construction. The air space between brick veneer and the supporting wall serves this purpose.

◆ Use a double layer of drywall on the interior surface.

◆ In exterior wall cavities, use acoustically absorbent fibrous insulation rather than closed-cell foams.

◆ Increasing the stud size from 38 x 89 mm (2 x 4 in.) to 38 x 140 mm (2 x 6 in.) improves noise reduction slightly.

Reduce the number of windows in the wall.

Mount interior drywall on resilient metal furring; double the layer for severe cases.

Cause

Noise transmitted through the roof or ceiling

Solutions

Make ventilation openings as small as possible. These openings will adversely affect the noise reduction properties of the roof system.

◆ Locate ventilation openings on the quiet side of the building, if possible.

◆ Use exposed fibrous insulation in the space between the roof and ceiling to improve noise reduction. Closed-cell foam does not effectively absorb sound.

◆ Use a double layer of drywall on ceilings.

◆ Use resilient metal furring to support ceiling drywall.

PROBLEM
TOO MUCH NOISE IN OUTDOOR SPACE (E.G., PATIO, BALCONY)

CAUSE

No effective noise barrier

SOLUTIONS

Place a barrier between the noise source and the affected area.

◆ Do not use hedges or trees as noise barriers. They do not reduce noise enough.

◆ Do not use a fence with gaps between the panels. A barrier must be "solid." Earth beams, buildings, and concrete walls are certainly acceptable, but lighter fences (sheet metal panels or 12-mm- [1/2-in.-] thick wood) are adequate for most cases.

◆ Make the barrier as high as possible to reduce the amount of noise bending over the top of the barrier.

◆ Make a barrier very long, or wrap it around the protected area to avoid noise coming around the ends.

CAUSE

Balcony exposed to loud noise

SOLUTIONS

Modify the balcony.

◆ If outdoor noise is slightly too high, use a solid balcony railing with an absorptive surface facing the balcony. Apply absorptive surface treatment to the underside of the balcony above and to any other balcony surfaces, if possible (see Figure 24).

◆ Possible absorptive treatments include perforated sheet metal with a fibrous sound absorber behind it and special concrete or wood-fibre panels used for highway noise barriers.

◆ If outdoor noise is much too high, fully enclose the balcony for use as a sun porch.

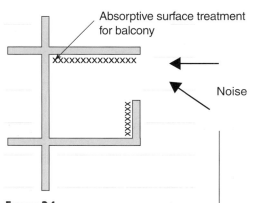

FIGURE 24
BALCONIES

Section 6.5 Outdoor Appliances
(Heat pumps, air conditioners, pool filters)

PROBLEM
NOISE ANNOYS NEIGHBOURS

CAUSE

Noise from an appliance in a quiet neighbourhood

SOLUTIONS

Select a quiet appliance.

◆ Check local noise bylaws. Typical bylaws specify the maximum acceptable noise at a lot boundary, either as a maximum sound level or relative to ambient noise caused by traffic and other distant sources.

◆ Select quiet appliances by checking manufacturers' literature for a noise rating.

◆ Heat pumps and air conditioners are commonly rated using Air-Conditioning and Refrigeration Institute (ARI) Standard 270-1984. Typical values are from 6 to 9 "bels." For a rough comparison with by-law requirements given in decibels, multiply the ARI sound rating by 10, and subtract 20 to get the noise at 4 m (13 ft.) from the unit.

◆ Do not attempt to reduce the noise output from a noisy appliance, unless the noise is due to an obvious fault like a rattling panel. Amateur modifications are unlikely to yield much noise reduction and may void the warranty.

CAUSE

Appliance in a poor location

SOLUTIONS

Move the appliance to a better location.

◆ Place the appliance as far from property boundaries as possible, or use a barrier to reduce sound reaching a nearby boundary.

◆ Do not locate a noisy appliance between close-spaced buildings, or under a carport or large roof overhang. Reflections from nearby surfaces increase the noise level and prevent barriers from working.

◆ If possible, locate the appliance near the corner of the home. In this location, a barrier connected to the corner of the house would be effective, if needed.

- Use the procedure in ARI Standard 275-1984 to assess possible locations for noise-rated appliances such as heat pumps. This allows for the effect of distance, nearby surfaces, and barriers. A similar but more complicated procedure is given in CSA Z107.71.

CAUSE

Poor location or noisy appliance

SOLUTIONS

Use a barrier or enclosure.

- Do not use an enclosure without expert advice to avoid interference with the normal operation of the appliance. This might void the warranty and reduce efficiency.
- Do not use an enclosure for a heat pump or an air conditioner, if the problem is the low-frequency hum heard inside an adjoining building. An enclosure is likely to amplify the hum.
- Use the procedure in ARI Standard 275-1984 to design a suitable barrier. Reflections from nearby walls may reduce the effect of a barrier.

Section 6.6 Indoor Appliances (Furnace, dishwasher, washing machine, ventilation fans)

PROBLEM

NOISE FROM A FORCED-AIR FURNACE

CAUSE

The fan or combustion systems of some modern high-efficiency furnaces are noisy.

SOLUTIONS

Modify the supply and return air ducts.

◆ Use a vibration break between the furnace and major ducts to stop vibrations from getting into the duct walls (see Figure 25).

◆ Fasten acoustic duct liner material (normally glass fibre with a special facing) on the inner surfaces of ducts to reduce transmission of noise along the ducts. Lining the large ducts closest to the furnace is usually enough. Make the duct cross section (with the lining installed) large enough for proper airflow.

◆ Locate the furnace as far as possible from rooms where quiet is important.

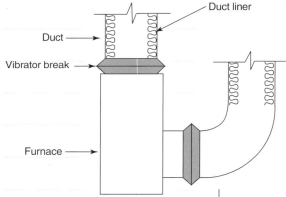

Duct liner

Duct

Vibrator break

Furnace

FIGURE 25
ADDING VIBRATOR BREAK TO FURNACE AIR DUCTS

PROBLEM

DUCTS CREAK OR BANG WHEN FURNACE CYCLES ON AND OFF

CAUSE

Expansion and contraction

SOLUTIONS

Operate the fan continuously to reduce expansion and contraction.

Modify the ducts.

◆ Put resilient pads between ducts and supports (see Figure 26).
◆ Add braces with resilient pads where panels flex. Identify suitable locations by listening or touching.
◆ Fasten acoustic duct liner to the inner face of ducts to reduce vibration of duct walls and noise transmission along the duct, as discussed above.

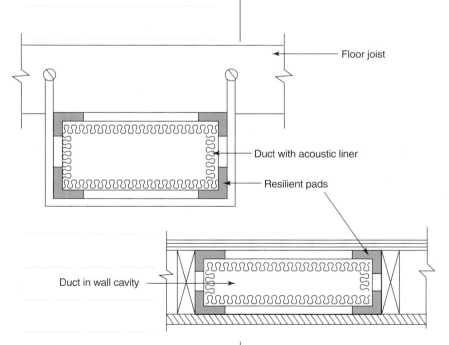

Floor joist

Duct with acoustic liner

Resilient pads

Duct in wall cavity

FIGURE 26
MODIFYING FURNACE AIR DUCTS

PROBLEM
Noisy appliances (dishwasher, washing machine)

CAUSE

Loud noise generation, poor location, poor installation

SOLUTIONS

Reduce transmission to other rooms.

◆ Install doors on the kitchen and the laundry room to reduce noise reaching other rooms.

◆ Locate rooms normally containing noisy appliances as far as possible from noise-sensitive areas.

Improve the installation.

◆ Put acoustically absorptive lining on the inner faces of any enclosure around the appliance.

◆ Do not connect an appliance to walls or cupboards; their surfaces act as sounding boards, and radiate more noise.

◆ Support any large appliance (such as a washing machine) resiliently on a heavy, rigid surface like a concrete floor, if possible.

◆ Use suitable resilient mounting to reduce vibration transfer into the structure. Incorrectly chosen mounting can amplify vibration; follow recommendations from the manufacturer or an expert. Resilient mounting is much less effective on flexible floors, such as plywood on wood joists.

PROBLEM
NOISY VENTILATION EQUIPMENT

CAUSE

Fan equipment

SOLUTIONS

◆ Use a better quality fan. Fans with low sone (noise rating) values are generally quieter.

◆ Move the fan away from the living area. It is preferable to install the fan in the basement and run the ducts from the fans to the kitchen or bathroom.

CAUSE

Ducts carry sound.

SOLUTIONS

◆ Install a flexible coupling between the ducts and the ventilation equipment.

CAUSE

Ventilation equipment connected directly to the building's structure

SOLUTIONS

◆ Avoid connecting the equipment directly to the structure. Mount the equipment (heat-recovery ventilator [HRV] or fan) on vibration isolation blocks (rubber blocks or springs) available from heating appliance distributors.

Section 6.7 Additional Reading

SOURCE	PUBLICATION
Canada Mortgage and Housing Corporation National Office 700 Montreal Road Ottawa ON K1A 0P7 613 748-2367	*Sound Transmission Through Floors: Phase III Summary Report,* 1993 *New Housing and Airport Noise,* 1981 NHA 5185 81/05 *Road and Rail Noise: Effects on Housing,* 1981 NHA 5156 81/10 *Flanking Sound Transmission in Wood Framed Construction,* 1993 *Research Report on Household Appliance Noise in Multi-Unit Buildings,* 1992 *Research Report on Plumbing Noise in Multi-Dwelling Buildings,* 1991 *Sound Performance of Wood Floor/Ceiling Assemblies: Stage II,* 1990 *Degradation of Wood Stud Wall Sound Insulation by Electrical Outlets,* 1993 *Sound Transmission Through Gypsum Board Walls,* IRC, 1994

SOURCE

Institute for Research in
Construction
National Research Council
of Canada
Institute for Research in
Construction
Publications Section
Ottawa ON K1A 0R6
In Ottawa: 613 993-2463
Other locations: 1 800 672-7990

PUBLICATION

"Introduction to Building
Acoustics," *Canadian Building
Digest* 236, 1985

"Factors Affecting Sound
Transmission Loss," *Canadian
Building Digest*, 239, 1985

"How to Reduce Noise
Transmission Between Homes
(Apartments)," Building
Practice Note 44, July 1983

"The Soundproof Basement,"
Building Practice Note 25,
December 1981

"Controlling Sound
Transmission into Buildings,"
Building Practice Note 56,
September 1985

Appendix A Noise Control for Walls

Wall Assembly No.	Section	Description	Typical 12.7-mm (1/2-in.) Type X gypsum board	STC 15.9-mm (5/8-in.) Type X gypsum board
Wall-1		• 38 x 89-mm (2 x 4-in.) studs spaced 400 mm (16 in.) or 600 mm (24 in.) O.C. • 89-mm (3-1/2-in.)-thick absorptive material • 1 layer of gypsum board on both sides	34	36
Wall-2		• 38 x 89-mm (2 x 4-in.) studs spaced 400 mm (16 in.) or 600 mm (24 in.) O.C. • 89-mm (3-1/2-in.) thick absorptive material • 2 layers of gypsum board on both sides	38	38
Wall-3		• 38 x 89-mm (2 x 4-in.) studs spaced 600 mm (24 in.) O.C. • 89-mm (3-1/2-in.) thick absorptive material • resilient metal channels on one side spaced 400 mm (16 in.) or 600 mm (24 in.) O.C. • 1 layer of gypsum board on both sides	43	48
Wall-4		• 38 x 89-mm (2 x 4-in.) studs spaced 600 mm (24 in.) O.C. • 89-mm (3-1/2-in.) thick absorptive material • resilient metal channels on one side spaced 400 mm (16 in.) or 600 mm (24 in.) O.C. • 1 layer of gypsum board on resilient metal channel side • 2 layers of gypsum board on other side	53	54
Wall-5		• 2 rolls of 38 x 89-mm (2 x 4-in.) staggered studs spaced 400 mm (16 in.) or 600 mm (24 in.) O.C. on a common 38 x 140-mm (2 x 6-in.) plate • 89-mm (3-1/2-in.)-thick absorptive material on one side or 65-mm (2-1/2-in.)-thick material on each side • 1 layer of gypsum board on both sides	45	47

Wall	Construction	Diagram		
Wall-6	• 2 rolls of 38 x 89-mm (2 x 4-in.) staggered studs spaced 400 mm (16 in.) or 600 mm (24 in.) O.C. on a common 38 x 140-mm (2 x 6-in.) plate • 89-mm (3-1/2-in.) thick absorptive material on one side or 65-mm (2-1/2-in.)-thick material on each side • 1 layer of gypsum board on one side • 2 layers of gypsum board on the other side		50	52
Wall-7	• 2 rolls of 38 x 89-mm (2 x 4-in.) staggered studs spaced 400 mm (16 in.) or 600 mm (24 in.) O.C. on a common 38 x 140-mm (2 x 6-in.) plate • 89-mm (3-1/2-in.)-thick absorptive material on one side or 65-mm (2-1/2-in.)-thick material on each side • 2 layers of gypsum board on both sides		55	56
Wall-8	• 2 rolls of 38 x 89-mm (2 x 4-in.) staggered studs spaced 400 mm (16 in.) or 600 mm (24 in.) O.C. on a common 38 x 140-mm (2 x 6-in.) plate • 89-mm (3-1/2-in.)-thick absorptive material on one side or 65-mm (2-1/2-in.)-thick material on each side • resilient metal channels on one side spaced 400 mm (16 in.) or 600 mm (24 in.) O.C. • 1 layer of gypsum board on resilient metal channel side		54	56
Wall-9	• 2 rolls of 38 x 89-mm (2 x 4-in.) staggered studs spaced 400 mm (16 in.) or 600 mm (24-in.) O.C. on a common 38 x 140-mm (2 x 6-in.) plate • 89-mm (3-1/2-in.) thick absorptive material on one side or 65-mm (2-1/2-in.)-thick material on each side • resilient metal channels on one side spaced 400 mm (16 in.) or 600 mm (24 in.) O.C. • 2 layers of gypsum board on each side		60	62

Wall Assembly No.	Section	Description	Typical 12.7-mm (1/2-in.) Type X gypsum board	STC 15.9-mm (5/8-in.) Type X gypsum board
Wall-10		• 2 rolls of 38 x 89-mm (2 x 4-in.) studs, each spaced 400 mm (16 in.) or 600 mm (24 in.) O.C. on separate 38 x 89-mm (2 x 4-in.) plates set 25 mm (1 in.) apart • 89-mm-thick absorptive material on both sides • 1 layer of gypsum board on each side	57	57
Wall-11		• 31 x 64-mm (2 x 3-in.) non-load-bearing steel studs spaced 600 mm (24 in.) O.C. • 65-mm (2-1/2-in.)-thick absorptive material • 1 layer of gypsum board on one side • 2 layers of gypsum board on the other side	50	50
Wall-12		• 31 x 92-mm (2 x 4-in.) non-load-bearing steel studs spaced 600 mm (24 in.) O.C. • 65-mm (2-1/2-in.)-thick absorptive material • 1 layer of gypsum board on one side • 2 layers of gypsum board on the other side	51	53
Wall-13		• 31 x 152-mm (2 x 6-in.) non-load-bearing steel studs spaced 600 mm (24 in.) O.C. • 65-mm (2-1/2-in.)-thick absorptive material • 1 layer of gypsum board on one side • 2 layers of gypsum board on the other side	54	55

Appendix B   Noise Control for Wood-Frame Floors

Floor	Construction (suggested minimum →)	STC 55	IIC 55	TMR[1] 50
Joist-1	• 16-mm (5/8-in.) tongue and groove plywood • 38 x 240-mm (2 x 10-in.) wood joists • 3 layers of 90-mm (3-1/2-in.)-thick glass fibre batts • 13-mm (1/2-in.) resilient metal channels, 600 mm (24 in.) O.C. • Two layers of 16 mm (5/8 in.) drywall	55	51	40
	Joist-1 + 9-mm (3/8-in.) foam undepad and carpet	58	80	72
	Joist-1 + 16-mm (5/8-in.) plywood raft on 6-mm (1/4-in.) felt	61	57	56
	Joist-1 + 18-mm (11/16-in.) Wonderboard screwed to plywood	62	53	53
Joist-2	• 16-mm (5/8-in.) tongue and groove plywood • 38 x 240-mm (2 x 10-in.) wood joists • 1 layer of 90-mm (3-1/2-in.)-thick glass fibre batts • 13-mm (1/2-in.) resilient metal channels, 600 mm (24-in.) O.C. • 1 layer of 16-mm (5/8-in.) drywall	49	44	33
	Joist-2 + 40-mm (1-1/2-in.) concrete on building paper	59	40	54
	Joist-2 + carpet on 40-mm (1-1/2-in.) concrete on building paper	59	73	54
	Joist-2 + carpet and underpad on 40-mm (1-1/2-in.) concrete on building paper	58	84	65

Floor		Construction	STC 55	IIC 55	TMR[1.] 50
Truss-1		• 16-mm (5/8-in.) tongue and groove plywood • 240-mm (10-in.)-deep wood floor trusses • 2 layers of glass fibre batts • 13-mm (1/2-in.) resilient metal channels, 600 mm (24 in.) O.C. • 1 layer of 16-mm (5/8-in.) drywall	48	40	43
		Truss-1 + carpet and underpad	50	66	55
		Truss-1 + 40-mm (1/2-in.) concrete on 25-mm (1-in.) high-density glass fibre board	60	52	51
Truss-2		• 16-mm (5/8-in.) tongue and groove plywood • 300-mm (12-in.)-deep wood floor trusses • 3 layers of glass fibre batts • 13-mm (1/2-in.) resilient metal channels, 600 mm (24 in.) O.C. • 1 layer of 16-mm (5/8-in.) drywall	55	48	37
		Truss-2 + carpet and underpad	56	72	54
		Truss-2 + 40-mm (1/2-in.) concrete on 25-mm (1-in.) high-density glass fibre board	62	59	55

[1.] Tapping machine rating (TMR) — For more information refer to CMHC research report "Sound Transmission Through Floors"

Conc-1					
		• 150-mm (6-in.) concrete slab	52		50
		Conc-1 + carpet and underpad	51	86	83
		Conc-1 + 40-mm (1-1/2-in.) concrete slab on 25-mm (1-in.) high-density glass fibre board	62	65	58
		Conc-1 + 16-mm (5/8-in.) plywood on 38 x 89-mm (2 x 4-in.) sleepers on 25-mm (1-in.) high-density glass fibre board	61	63	56